Hap[p

Ten Poe[

about Bicycles

Kane
x x x
ü

ex libris

Candlestick Press

Published by:

Candlestick Press,
Diversity House, 72 Nottingham Road, Arnold, Nottingham UK NG5 6LF
www.candlestickpress.co.uk

Design and typesetting by Diversity Creative Marketing Solutions Ltd.,
www.diversity.agency

Printed by Ratcliff & Roper Print Group, Nottinghamshire, UK

Cover illustration © Rosalind Bliss, 2009

Candlestick Press monogram © Barbara Shaw, 2008

© Candlestick Press, 2009 and 2018

Second edition, revised 2018

Reprinted 2019, 2021

ISBN 978 1 907598 66 1

Acknowledgements:

The publisher acknowledges with thanks the estate of Michael Donaghy
and Pan Macmillan, London, for permission to print 'Machines'
from *Remembering Dances Learned Last Night*, Picador, 2000; Paul
McLoughlin and Shoestring Press for permission to print 'The Bicycle
Garden', from *What Moves Moves*, Shoestring Press, 2004; Helena
Nelson for 'Bike with no Hands', from *Starlight on Water*, The Rialto;
James Roderick Burns and *Fire* for permission to print 'Boy on a
Bicycle'; Jonathan Davidson for 'A Lady Cyclist Learns To Cycle'
from *Moving the Stereo*, Jackson's Arm, 1993; Connie Bensley and
Bloodaxe Books for 'Wheel Fever' from *Choosing to be a Swan*,
Bloodaxe Books, 1994; Jonathan Edwards and Seren Books for 'Nun
on a Bicycle', *My Family & Other Superheroes* (Seren, 2014); the
Estate of MK Joseph for permission to use 'Girl, Boy, Flower, Bicycle'
by MK Joseph, Inscription on a *Paper Dart: Selected Poems 1945-1972*
(AUP; OUP, 1974) and Jacqueline Gabbitas for 'Riding Down Hill with
No Brakes to Talk of', as yet unpublished, with thanks also to Martin
Parker for the artworking of this poem in bicycle form. Derek Mahon,
'The Bicycle', is from *Collected Poems* (1999) by kind permission of
the author and The Gallery Press.

Where poets are no longer living, their dates are given.

Contents

A Lady Cyclist Learns to Cycle

(England, 1917)

They led it round the yard and garden
on a long rein.
They fed it oil.

It was black as my jet black boots,
heavy as a gate.
It ticked, shone.

Climbing on it, I felt it shy,
lunge beneath me,
clatter to earth.

They held me up, the men, laughing,
shouldered me round,
gentlemanly.

The guns of Passchendaele bellowed.
The men held me.
It shook, I shook,

but when they let go, I did not
let go, but moved
forward, shouting.

Jonathan Davidson

Boy on a Bicycle

A boy rides a bicycle before the first world war. He is eighteen, almost nineteen – a man, really – and wears his new uniform with pride. He is cycling along an embankment on the outskirts of a small town. The sun is halfway towards noon, the wind tousling his light brown hair; his pinkish lips are mouthing a music-hall ditty under his sparse moustache. He is going to see a girl he used to know.

He has no idea he will be dead in a week, his legs thrown out the wrong way under a snarl of barbed wire. Now he marvels at the warmth of his muscles as the chain drives the wheels around. Now his tongue tastes of mint and apples.

James Roderick Burns

Girl, Boy, Flower, Bicycle

This girl
Waits at the corner for
This boy
Freewheeling on his bicycle.
She holds
A flower in her hand
A gold flower
In her hands she holds
The sun.
With power between his thighs
The boy
Comes smiling to her
He rides
A bicycle that glitters like
The wind.
This boy this girl
They walk
In step with the wind
Arm in arm
They climb the level street
To where
Laid on the glittering handlebars
The flower
Is round and shining as
The sun.

MK Joseph (1914 – 1981)

Nun on a Bicycle

Now here she comes, rattling over cobbles,
powered by her sandals, the gentle downhill
and the grace of God. Now here she comes, her habit

what it was always waiting to become:
a slipstream. Past stop signs, the pedestrian
traffic at rush hour, the humdrum mopeds,

on a day already thirty in the shade:
with her robe fluttering like solid air,
she makes her own weather. Who could blame her,

as the hill sharpens, she picks up speed and smiles
into her future, if she interrupted
the *Our Fathers* she's saying in her head,

to say *Whee*, a gentle *Whee*, under her breath?
O cycle, Sister! Look at you now, freewheeling
through the air conditioning of the morning –

who's to say the God who isn't there
isn't looking down on you and grinning?

Jonathan Edwards

Wheel Fever

Frank Reynolds has ordered a Coventry,
48 inches high and with all
the new improvements.

But it cost £14, and I am afraid
to sink so much money – it would be almost
three months of my salary.

All the fellows in the village
have bicycle fever, and none
more than myself.

        *

Rode on Aubrey's wooden cycle
into Warboys, to see a Spider-Wheel
which Monty has for sale.

But the tyres were tied on
with pieces of twine, so I did not
part with my cash.

        *

I've done it! I could not bear to wait
any longer. I now possess a Coventry
(without the new improvements).

Before I paid, I took it for a spin
but lost the treadle,
landed in a heap

and had to have it taken back
in the cart, and put together.
But after that

I rode off round the lanes
as right as twelve o'clock
and pleased as Punch.

*

Coming back from a spin today, I met
Mr Dodds with his cartload of bread.
He must have known

that horses shy at bicycles, but
he did not get down, and sure enough
his wretched animal

reared, backed into the dyke, and emptied
22 stone of bread and 6 stone of flour
into the water.

*

Set out with James Black, to ride
to the prayer meeting, but
by Redman's corner

he ran into me, knocked me off,
broke my handle, bent my treadle, and fell
on top of me.

*

I am receiving unpleasant letters from
Mr Dodds. I do not believe that flour
can be so dear.

Unlike Aubrey or Frank Reynolds,
I can now ride my bicycle
with arms folded.

*

I was riding my bicycle with my arms
folded on my way to Doddington,
when I hit a stone

and pitched on my head. Managed to get up
and stagger on, covered with blood
and feeling faint.

Of course I could not help Uncle
in the shop. The carrier put his pony in
and took me home.

*

Could not move this morning, so stiff
and sore. My bicycle will take three days
to put right.

I miss it dreadfully. Frank Reynolds
does not seem keen on the idea
of lending me his.

But I have had a carrot poultice put on
my eye and I shall soon be fit enough
to ride again.

Connie Bensley

Bike with no Hands

One look at you and I knew
you'd be able to ride a bike with no hands.

I tried it, of course, but could never do it.
It was written all over your face that you
would have practised, bare legs, bloody knees,
in the summer evenings, hours at a time
when no-one was watching the mishaps, until
casually, coolly, at infinite ease,
you'd ride, no-handed, surveying the street,
as if you'd been born on a circus bike.

I wish – but then, we are what we are.
I drive with two hands, walk with both feet
firmly planted on sensible ground. And
I've got you. You can ride with no hands.

Helena Nelson

Sometimes it felt like the handlebars were alive

But the crossbar was an island, heavy and still,

Sometimes it felt like the back wheel went faster than the front and I would catch myself up in time.

while all around me

snapping round my wrists –

– their tongues electrician's tape!

whipped my hair onto my face.

and the wind

colour and blur,

Riding Down Hill with No Brakes to Talk of

Jacqueline Gabbitas

The Bicycle Garden

The graves of children who go missing
are abandoned bicycles set in concrete
bases lowered into shallow trenches
by the railway bridge and left to rust.
The engineer (retired) who tends
the place says visitors are few –
he imagines parents driving slowly by
or peering through the wire-mesh fence
for a particular shade of paint or rake
of handlebar, but they don't come in.

And there it was, this gaunt tableau
of BMXs, racers, mountain bikes,
an aged Vespa with its fairing crushed,
and tricycles with tassels tied to handle grips
or crossbars, where they stayed, seeming,
to those who looked, to rise up from the ground
or sink into it. You turn away –

because there's no such garden, though
the bicycles are often all that's found.
An end-page columnist invented it
when it seemed to him society
was waging war on being young,
on children who enticed and let you
down. So he dreamed a garden for them,
and the engineer was somehow odd
enough to make the whole thing real,
a sleight that left its maker lying
with the silence in his ears, as if
some violence had been done.

Paul McLoughlin

Machines

Dearest, note how these two are alike:
This harpsichord pavane by Purcell
And the racer's twelve-speed bike.

The machinery of grace is always simple.
This chrome trapezoid, one wheel connected
To another of concentric gears,
Which Ptolemy dreamt of and Schwinn perfected,
Is gone. The cyclist, not the cycle, steers.
And in the playing, Purcell's chords are played away.

So this talk, or touch if I were there,
Should work its effortless gadgetry of love,
Like Dante's heaven, and melt into the air.

If it doesn't, of course, I've fallen. So much is chance,
So much agility, desire, and feverish care,
As bicyclists and harpsichordists prove

Who only by moving can balance,
Only by balancing move.

Michael Donaghy (1954 – 2004)

The Bicycle

There was a bicycle, a fine
Raleigh with five gears
And racing handlebars.
It stood at the front door
Begging to be mounted;
The frame shone in the sun.

I became like a character
In The Third Policeman, half
Human, half bike, my life
A series of dips and ridges,
Happiness a free-wheeling
Past fragrant hawthorn hedges.

Cape and sou'wester streamed
With rain as I rode to school
Side-tracking the bus routes.
Night after night I dreamed
Of valves, pumps, sprockets,
Reflectors and repair kits.

Soon there were long rides
In the country, wet weekends
Playing cards in the kitchens
Of mountain youth hostels,
Day-runs to Monaghan,
Rough and exotic roads.

It went with me to Dublin
Where I sold it the same winter;
But its wheels still sing
In the memory, stars that turn
About an eternal centre,
The bright spokes glittering.

Derek Mahon (1941 – 2020)

COMING TO

AN LA LOVERS BOOK

BY JOURDYN KELLY

Coming To

ISBN Number - 978-0-9982725-6-6

Cover Art by: Jourdyn Kelly
Interior Design by: Drue Hoffman, Buoni Amici Press

ALSO BY JOURDYN KELLY

EVE SUMPTOR NOVELS:

Something About Eve

Flawed Perfection

The Truth About Eve

THE DESTINED SERIES:

Destined to Kill

Destined to Love

Destined to Meet

THE LA LOVERS SERIES:

Coming Home

Fifty Shades of Pink

Coming Out

Becoming

Coming To

I miss you, Momma. I love you.

CHAPTER ONE

"Dyke!"

Dani Reed snarled and flipped up both her middle fingers before grabbing her crotch.

"You're just sorry you can never have this!" she yelled back at her hecklers. She tried hard to ignore their continued taunts. It wasn't easy. Every day it was something with them. They criticized her "boy" haircut, her choice to wear "boy" clothes, and the way she looked at girls like a "boy" would. It pissed her off. Who were they to say that she couldn't dress the way she wanted? Or look at girls? Girls were undoubtedly much better than those stupid boys.

"Why do you let them get to you?"

Claire Oliver strode up to her best friend, nudging Dani so she would stop interacting with the assholes who were making fun of her.

"They don't," Dani sulked. "But you just made them think they did. You should have let me say what I needed to say."

"You weren't *saying* anything. You were grabbing your crotch and making rude gestures. I don't like that, Dani."

"And I don't like them shitting on me every chance they get." She eyed Claire discreetly. She wore a skirt today, showing off her pale legs. Her strawberry blonde hair was up in a cute ponytail with two strands falling down to frame her heart-shaped face. God, Dani was so in love with her best friend. She could never tell Claire that, of course. But she sure as hell could pretend they were girlfriend and girlfriend walking to Claire's car so they could go home from school together. No matter how she felt about Claire, she couldn't help being a little mad that she had just reprimanded her. "You gonna tell me that if I dressed like a girl, they'd leave me alone?"

"Have I *ever* said that to you?" Claire rolled her eyes. Sometimes she thought Dani argued with her for the sake of arguing. The girl had a chip on her shoulder the size of Texas. Not that Claire blamed her. She supposed anyone would be angry having to deal with bullies all the time.

"No," Dani sulked. She felt the need to yell, scream, and shout, but Claire never took the bait. Eh, it was fine. Claire wasn't the one she was pissed at anyway. Plus, she didn't want her best friend/dream girlfriend mad at her.

"What are you up to tonight?" Claire asked amicably. She had known Dani since she was seven years old. She'd like to think she had a good handle on how to change the sullen attitude Dani often got in.

Dani shrugged. "Studying."

Claire laughed. "You are such a liar! You're going to go home, throw on some boxers, and play video games until your stomach yells at you for not feeding it."

Dani grinned. "If you knew that, why'd you ask?"

"I wanted to see if you'd own up to it."

"Yeah, well, I bet you're going to be studying all night."

"Maybe."

Claire's non-committal answer gave Dani pause. Their routines had been consistent over the past ten years. If they weren't physically together, they were on the phone. Claire would study and give Dani pop quizzes to see if she was paying attention. Dani would play games and talk about the worlds she lost herself in. There had never been a "maybe" in their routine. Ever.

"What do you mean maybe?"

"I didn't mean anything by it, Dani."

Dani stopped. She watched the sway of Claire's hips. The way her skirt swished the back of her thighs. Usually, that would ground her, allowing her to forget everything wrong in the world. Right now, it wasn't helping at all. Something was up, and Dani wanted to know what it was. Now.

"Claire?"

Claire sighed and turned back to face Dani. "I have a date tonight."

Dani's stomach began to ache so bad she felt like she could throw up. *That's not your stomach, stupid. Your heart just shattered.*

"Oh." She should have known this would happen. She was such a fucking idiot. Claire was a senior — a year ahead of Dani — the prom was coming up, and Claire was fucking hot. What did she think? That Claire would realize that she was as gay as Dani was and declare her undying love? Dani scoffed at herself. *Idiot*, she reiterated silently. "Cool. Look, I'm going to, uh, I forgot something in my locker. Go on ahead. I'll call you tomorrow or something."

"Dani! I'm your ride! How are you going to get home?"

Claire teared up as she watched Dani take off in an all-out sprint. She hadn't meant to break it to her like that. What she had *wanted* was *not* to go on this date. But she wasn't as brave as Dani was. Dani didn't care what people thought of her masculine clothes, spiked hair, and obvious gayness. Except for her mom. Ever since Dani's father died, Dani had "toned down" her need to "be herself" when she was at home. She said it was because her mom was still mourning her dad. Claire had her own theories. One of which was Dani's mom was a controlling bitch.

Dani had been super close to her father. When he died, a part of her did, too. She used to tell Claire that he understood her. That if she were to come out to him, he would still be proud of her. Never once did she say that about her mom. In fact, Dani said she thought her mom blamed Dani in some way for her father's death. She never said it outright, but the anger she had said it all. She was the *only* one in the world that didn't know — or pretended not to know — Dani liked girls.

On the flip side, *no one*, not even Dani knew that Claire was the same. You'd think she'd be able to tell her best friend at least, but no. Every time she tried, she chickened out. Claire told herself it was because she wasn't ready yet. The reality was, she saw every day how people treated Dani. Claire's skin wasn't thick enough to withstand that. Plus, she had a massive crush on Dani. If she couldn't handle the bullying, she sure as hell couldn't handle the rejection of knowing Dani didn't feel the same way about her.

"Stupid, stupid, stupid!" Dani kicked a shell, unsatisfied with its gentle tumble into the ocean. The tide was low, and Dani found herself in her favorite spot amongst the seaweed and barnacles under the pier. Not even Claire knew about this place.

Which was a good thing right now since Dani didn't want to see the cheating . . . nope, not going there. This wasn't on Claire. If Dani had wanted Claire to know how she felt about her, she would have had the balls to say something.

Dani dug her bare toes in the sand, allowing herself to sink in. Maybe she would get stuck, and the tide would come in. If she drowned, she wouldn't have to see Claire go out on a date with some asshole. Or kiss some asshole. Or get married to some asshole. Or have kids with some asshole. She shuddered at that thought. Kids meant sex. Sex with some asshole. She dug in more, sinking further. *Take me now.*

"Hey, Dad. So, uh, I think I'm ready to join you now. Got room up there?" Dani sniffled. "Do they even take gay people up there? Cuz a whole lotta people don't think so down here. Doesn't matter." She bent to pick up a shell and threw it in the water. "I don't care where I go. Hell has to be better than watching Claire date some dude. She's going to, like, fall in love with him and forget all about me."

With effort, she pulled her feet from the sand and sat down, not caring that her cargo shorts were getting wet. She wished her dad was here. Cancer had taken him from her a little more than a year ago. It sucked. It sucked even more that she couldn't help but feel life had taken away the wrong parent. Forget being gay; she was probably going to hell for that thought alone. But she had been able to talk to her dad. She felt comfortable with him. She never said the words "I'm gay" out loud to him, but Dani was sure he knew. Her mom was just so . . . so damn mean! *Nothing* Dani did was right. She'd probably have a coronary if she found out Dani liked the ladies. Okay, *one* lady. Who was going on a fucking date with someone that wasn't her!

"Ugh! Why can't she see she should be with me? It's not fair, Dad." She picked at the barnacles. "I wish you and I had talked more about dating and stuff. Maybe you could have told me what to expect from girls. Then again, you ended up with Mom. Though," she chuckled, "I can't imagine Mom being a girl. What am I going to do? How the hell do I sit around and watch the girl I love fall for someone else?" She banged her head against the pier post. "One and a half more years. Then I can get out of here. Maybe I'll join the army or something. Anything to get away from seeing Claire with . . . not me."

Her phone buzzed in one of the many pockets she had, but she ignored it. If it was her mom, she didn't feel like being yelled at. If it was Claire, she didn't feel like hearing about the stupid date. Man, she needed more friends. Claire had a ton of other friends. Dani only needed Claire. Or so she thought. What was she going to do now that she had no one? Of course, Claire would tell her she would always be her friend. But Claire didn't realize how much that hurt.

"Come on, Dani. Answer the phone!" Claire threw her phone on the bed and stomped around the room. Damn peer pressure! If her friends hadn't practically agreed to this date themselves, she wouldn't be going through this heartache now. She didn't even like Noah. He was an arrogant jock. He literally couldn't believe Claire had turned him down the first few times he'd asked her out. When her other friends found out he liked her, they wouldn't shut up about how cute and popular he was. She didn't even care about being popular! She just didn't want to be a bullied outcast. Unfortunately, she felt like her friends were beginning to think she and Dani were together. That scared her enough to agree to a stupid date. *Coward.*

Claire's phone buzzed and she leaped onto the bed to get it. When it wasn't from Dani, she groaned and collapsed heavily onto her pillow. She held the phone up to her face and read the text from Noah.

Pick U up @ 7. B ready.

Claire rolled her eyes. "*Yes, sir!*" she mumbled sarcastically. Ugh, she really didn't need this crap. Not from him or Dani. Forget them both!

Sorry, I have to cancel. Claire sent the text before she could talk herself out of it.

Y???

Not feeling well.

U were fine earlier

Well, now I'm not.

Y are u such a bitch?

"Why are *you* such an asshole?" Claire said out loud but refrained from actually typing the words.

R u like that dyke or something?

Claire's heart began to pound. She almost, *almost* changed her mind about the date just to show him she wasn't gay. Then she remembered the look on Dani's face. Claire didn't know why that stuck with her. Maybe it was wishful thinking. Whatever it was, it — and the fact that she hated Noah for talking negatively about Dani — gave her courage.

You're an asshole, Noah. You think that just because a girl doesn't want to go out with you, she's gay? Could your ego BE any bigger? Don't text me anymore.

Okay, so she didn't come out. But she didn't *go* out either. She was going to put that in the win column. Now, if she could get Dani to answer her damn calls.

Each time she ignored one of Claire's calls, Dani's heart broke a little more. The only other time she didn't speak to Claire was when they were ten, and Claire took a video cartridge out of the game console. *While* Dani was playing it! All that progress had been lost, and Dani punished Claire for an entire week. Six days. Four days. It was three. Hours. *Three* hours was all she could hold out for before *she* was the one asking Claire for forgiveness.

Dani looked at her watch. It had been three hours and seventeen minutes since she had run like a coward away from Claire. There! She had a new record. She could keep this going, right? Besides, shouldn't Claire be on her *date*?

Answer your damn phone, Dani!

Dani's eyes popped open. Claire didn't curse at her! *She* was the curser! Dammit.

It's rude to text while on your date

You're not dead. Good. Now I can kill you myself! I didn't go on the stupid date.

Dani jumped up from her spot. "What? Why?" She rolled her eyes when she realized Claire couldn't hear a damn word she was saying.

What? Y? She backspaced. **Why?** Claire hated "text speak." She didn't think people needed to be dumbed down any further.

Does it matter? I've been trying to call you for hours. Where are you?

Dani looked around her. She was under a pier, the tide was coming up, water was creeping up her legs, and a crab was riding the small waves that were ebbing and flowing.

I'll be there in about thirty minutes.

CHAPTER TWO

She was nervous as hell and didn't know why. Dani had stood at Claire's front door like a million times. Why did *this* time feel different? *Don't be stupid.* You *aren't her date. Don't forget she's pissed at you.*

Claire opened the door to find Dani staring off into space.

"Why are you all wet?"

"Huh?" Dani blinked at Claire then looked down at herself. *Oh yeah.* "Um."

Claire tapped her toe, her hands planted firmly on her hips and waited for Dani to explain herself. When she got nothing more than an "um," she rolled her eyes.

"Mom! I'm going over to Dani's!" She grabbed Dani's hand and dragged her with her. "You have exactly eight minutes and thirty-four seconds to come up with an explanation."

Dani had every right to be upset with how Claire was talking to her. But all she could think about was how Claire was holding her hand. Okay, *technically*, they weren't holding hands. Whatever. In Dani's mind, this was their first romantic moment. It didn't matter that Claire was muttering or squeezing the life out of Dani's hand. Nope. They were touching, and Claire hadn't let go yet. And she didn't until they got to Dani's front porch.

"Did you come up with an answer?" Claire asked sharply.

"Um."

Claire huffed. "Do you have your keys, or do I need to run home and get mine?"

"I have mine."

"Oh, look! You *can* speak!"

"Come on, Claire." Dani fished her keys out of her pocket and unlocked the door. "Why are you busting my balls."

"You don't have balls." *Thank God.* "And you had me worried about you! Since when do you not answer my calls?"

"Since you ruined . . . my game." *Whew! Good save, Dani girl.*

"What?"

"When you took out the game when I was playing it," Dani said with exasperation.

"Dani Reed! That was *six* years ago!"

"Yeah, well. I'm just sayin'. It's not like I've never, you know, not spoken to you before."

Claire let out a groan of frustration and pushed past Dani once the door was open. "You are the most infuriating, stubborn . . ." She marched straight towards Dani's bedroom.

"Why aren't you on your date again?" Dani grumbled.

"Because," Claire drawled. "I was worried about you. You just ran off and then ignored my calls and texts."

"Maybe I wanted to be alone. Ever think of that?"

"That's not how we do things, Dani. You and I, we *talk.*" Yeah, she realized she was a hypocrite. Whatever.

"Wanting to be alone means not wanting to talk. Obvs."

"Don't you "obvs" me! And don't sit down on your bed!"

Dani jumped up, her hands in karate chop position, ready to fight whatever was about to bite her ass. "Why? What?"

"You have sand all over you." Claire bit her lip to keep from laughing. Dani was so cute. Almost too cute to be mad at. Almost.

"Geez, Claire! I thought there was a spider or some shit!"

"Will you go change, please, so we can talk."

Dani crossed her arms defiantly. "Are you going to stop yelling at me?"

"Are you going to start saying more than "um" and "uh" when I ask you questions?" Claire countered.

"I don't know. Depends on what you ask."

"Ugh. Go change. *Please.*"

Dani hesitated for a split second, then grabbed her boxers and a t-shirt and headed off towards the bathroom. *Not* because Claire told her to, but because she had sand in places she didn't need sand. That was her story, and she was sticking to it.

Claire shook her head, and even though she was alone now, she hid her smile. She took the time alone to look at her surroundings. She had been in Dani's room countless times before. For some reason, this felt different. How had she never noticed how messy Dani was? Perhaps messy wasn't the right word. Clothes may have been on chairs and the desk, but they were folded. Games were everywhere, but in such a weird order that Claire didn't understand. Though, if she were to move one, Dani would go crazy and immediately put it back where it was. She had a "system" that she didn't want messed with. The bed, however, was always made, which tickled Claire for some reason. Orderly chaos.

Claire found herself staring at the bed for far longer than she should. She and Dani had slept together in the double bed many times. She distinctly remembered the moment their friendly sleep-over became more for her. When the charcoal sheets became too heavy and the heat of Dani's body next to her too hot.

"May I sit on *my* bed now?"

Claire nearly jumped out of her skin. "Um, yeah." She deliberately avoided looking at Dani in her boxers and t-shirt — no bra — as she sat in the chair farthest from the bed. Why the hell was this getting to her now? She had been hiding how she felt for Dani for years. She was an old pro at it. Until now, obviously. Was it because she was graduating soon? Dani still had a year left to go in high school.

Meanwhile, Claire would be going to college. Were these overwhelming feelings for Dani a manifestation of Claire's fear that they would lose touch with each other? *Psychology should be on my list of majors*, Claire thought humorously.

Dani narrowed her eyes at her best friend. "Why are you smiling?"

Dammit. "Just thinking about you going all Kung Fu on a non-existent spider."

"Kung Fu," Dani muttered. "Not my fault you scared the shit out of me. So, why didn't you go on your date?" She hoped she didn't sound as bitter as she felt.

"Where did you go?"

Dani sulked. "Why do you always do that? Every time I ask you a question, you ask one back instead of answering."

Because I'm not ready to answer questions yet. "I was worried about you, Dani. When you didn't answer my calls or texts, I decided to cancel my plans. I was about to go out and look for you when you *finally* answered. So? Where did you go, and why did you run away from me?"

Dani shrugged then saw Claire's angry look. "I didn't *run* away. I told you I forgot something . . ."

"Dani."

Dani sighed. "Fine. I just wanted to be alone for a while. And, you know, talk to Dad."

Claire's face softened. It always broke her heart when Dani spoke of her dad. She wondered why Dani never told her she still talked to him.

"I called a few of our usual places. No one saw you."

"I didn't go anywhere, really." Underneath a desolate pier wasn't anywhere, was it? "I, like, have this spot when I need to be alone." *Don't tell her that! She'll want to go!* The devil on Dani's shoulder chastised her for giving up that information. The other side — she didn't think she had an angel side, so this was just the slightly more emotional side — wanted Claire to know *everything.*

"Oh." Claire couldn't deny it hurt that Dani had a special place all her own. But it made sense. Homelife with Dani's mom wasn't the greatest. During the week, it wasn't so bad because Dani had school, and her mom worked the night shift. Their paths rarely crossed. The weekends were a different story. If Dani's mom was home, Dani spent most of her time with Claire. The only time they weren't together was when Claire had some family thing she couldn't get out of.

"Sorry," Dani muttered.

"For what? Having a place of your own?" Claire clicked her tongue. "You don't have to be sorry. I totally understand."

"You do?"

"Sure."

"Do you have a place, too?"

"Not really," Claire answered carefully. "I mean, I have my room. But I don't think I need it as much as you do, you know?"

"Yeah." Dani scooted back on her bed until her feet hung inches from the floor. She began to swing her feet in weird patterns out of nervousness. "Who were you going out with?"

"Does it matter?"

Dani looked up at Claire, who seemed to be a bit embarrassed. "It does to me."

"Why?" Claire sighed when Dani flopped back on her bed in frustration. "I'm not trying to be difficult, Dani. I'm just trying to figure . . . things out."

Dani propped herself up on her elbows. "What things?"

"Things like why you ran away from me when I told you I had a date. Why did you need to be alone? Why did you need to talk to your dad?"

"That's a lot of things." Dani laid back down and stared up at the ceiling. "If I answer your questions, will you answer mine?"

"If I can."

"That's not fair, Claire." Dani chuckled at her little rhyme. "Fair Claire."

Claire smiled at Dani's silliness. Maybe it was time to start being honest with her best friend. Worst case scenario, they stop being friends. Okay, that was excruciating to think about. But if she considered the fact that she would be graduating and going to college, she would live. Right?

"Fine," she said finally. "Answer *one* question honestly, and I'll answer anything you want to ask me."

Dani sat up. "Anything?"

Claire nodded.

"'Kay. Which one do you want me to answer?"

"Do you like me?"

Dani's mouth went dry. She tried to swallow, but there was nothing to swallow. If she opened her mouth, she was pretty sure dust would puff out. Of course, she knew what Claire was asking, but Dani went with the "play dumb" sarcasm.

"Duh. You're my best friend."

Claire's nostrils flared. "You know what I mean, Dani. Do you need me to write a note with checkboxes?"

"Ask me anything else, and I'll answer. I swear!"

Claire got up from her chair and walked towards the bed. She had no clue where this rush of confidence came from, but she was going to take advantage of it.

"Dani, do you have feelings for me?"

Dani hung her head. She wouldn't be able to handle the disgust or disappointment on Claire's face when she told the truth.

"*Yes.*"

Claire looked up at the heavens — or the ceiling of Dani's room which had glow in the dark stars — and mouthed a *thank God!* She sat down next to Dani on the bed.

"Why didn't you tell me?"

"Uh, because I'm not stupid. I didn't want to be one of those pathetic lesbians who falls for their straight bestie."

"What if I'm not?"

"Not what? My bestie?"

Claire rolled her eyes. Dani was smart, but sometimes she just needed a little push.

"Dani?"

It took some effort, but Dani looked over at Claire. When Claire leaned towards her, Dani froze. Then it happened. Something she never thought would happen in a million years.

Claire kissed her. It wasn't sexy or romantic. It was *barely* a kiss because their noses bumped.

"Uh, Claire? What's going on?"

"Have you ever kissed anyone?"

Great. More questions instead of answers. "No."

"Me, either."

Dani's eyebrows shot up. "Really?"

"Do you think I'm going behind the bleachers at school or something?"

"Or something," Dani muttered. "You had a date."

"That I *didn't* go on," Claire reminded her.

"Oh yeah." She shook her head. *Get back to the kiss!* "I don't understand why you're kissing *me*. Is this like an experiment or something?" Dani frowned. "Did your other friends put you up to this?" She looked around. "Is this on Snapchat?"

"I can't believe you think I'd do something like that to you."

"Well, I can't believe you're kissing me! You're straight . . ."

"No, I'm not!" Claire yelled. "I'm not straight, Dani! *That's* what I'm trying to show you!"

Dani blinked. "Since when?"

"Uh, *birth!*"

Dani popped off the bed and began storming around the room. "Why didn't you tell me? All this time, I thought I was alone! All this time I've been listening to stupid kids call me names and make fun of me . . ."

"That's why," Claire said softly. "I'm not as strong as you, Dani. I couldn't fight back like you do. If people said those things to me or about me, I'd be devastated."

"You don't think it hurts me, Claire? All the stupid things they say?"

"You don't act like it. You just give it back to them like it doesn't faze you."

Dani shrugged. "That's what you have to do with bullies like that. The only one who can give their words power is you. Of course, it gets on my nerves constantly having to listen to their crap. But I'm not ashamed of who I am, Claire. Except maybe here at home," she finished quietly.

"I think that's different, Dani. You're not ashamed, just scared maybe."

"It's stupid. Why should a kid be afraid of their parents? You know, if Dad were alive, I bet he'd understand and be supportive."

"I'm sure he would."

Dani looked back at Claire, who was still sitting on her bed. Isn't this what she had always wanted? Claire was there on her bed. She had kissed her. She had come out to her. And what was Dani doing? Trying to find reasons they shouldn't be doing it! Was she freakin' crazy?

"I'm sorry for accusing you of . . . I'm sorry for being stupid." Dani sat back down next to Claire and reached for her hand. "I know you'd never do that to me. It's just, I've been dreaming about this for, like, ten years. It kinda scared me when you kissed me."

"Scared you? Why?"

"Cuz, I never thought it was possible. I was all emo with unrequited love and stuff and then BOOM! Out of the blue, your lips are on mine. Kinda."

Claire giggled. "We could try again if you like."

"Yes! I mean, uh," Dani lowered her voice. "Yes. Please."

Claire giggled again and shook her head. "Okay, ahem." She

scooted closer to Dani. "There has to be some trick to this, right? You go that way, and I'll go this way."

Dani nodded, not realizing how close Claire was already until they bumped heads.

"Ow."

"That's not the way I said to go," Claire teased as she rubbed her forehead.

"Sorry," Dani grinned. "Come on. We can do this. Though it'd probably be much easier if we didn't have noses."

Claire scrunched *her* nose and squinted her eyes.

"What are you doing?" Dani asked.

"Trying to imagine you without a nose."

Dani covered her face. "Stop it!"

Claire took Dani's hands and pulled them down. Once again, she leaned in — hoping Dani would remember which way to go — and pressed her lips to Dani's. This time, there was full contact. Her tummy did somersaults. Her face felt as though it was on fire. And her heart . . . oh, her heart *finally* felt free.

"Whoa." Dani blew out a breath. Holy crap! If she'd known that kissing Claire would make her feel like *that*, she would have taken the chance years ago! Had her heart even beat before that kiss? Had she even *breathed* before that kiss? *Then* she thought about her breath. *Oh, man! Does my breath stink?*

"Whoa is right," Claire said a bit breathlessly. "Again?"

"Uh, call your mom and tell her you're staying over. We're doing that, like, all night long."

Claire placed her hand on Dani's chest when she leaned in again. "I'm not ready for anything else, Dani. I mean, I've thought about it with you, but . . ."

"Oh! No! I didn't . . . crap . . . I didn't mean it that

way. Listen, I get it, okay? I don't think I'm ready, either. I just wanted to spend more time with you and practice kissing. I wasn't trying to pressure you into anything. I swear."

Claire gave Dani a sweet smile. "I know. I just wanted to be upfront with you. I guess the more we talk, the less headaches we'll have."

"Cool. So, um . . . does this mean you're, like, my girlfriend now?"

"Do you want me to be?"

"Duh. I have since we met."

"Really? That long?"

Dani rolled her eyes. "Yes, *that* long. So?"

Claire pursed her lips. "I still don't know if I'm ready for people to know about me, Dani."

"We don't have to, like, hold hands at school or anything. I just want us to be together. At least for the rest of the school year."

Claire's eyebrows raised. "You only want me to be your girlfriend for a couple of months?"

"No! It just sucks that you decide to let me know all this right before you graduate and go off to college."

"Dani, I'm staying here for college." She turned, bringing one of her legs up under her on the bed. "Do you really think I would do all this and then leave? I'm beginning to think you don't know me at all."

"Well, I didn't know you were gay!"

"Okay, I'll give you that. But we've talked about college before. You know UCLA is my choice."

"I know." Dani sighed. "What if you meet someone there?"

"What if someone transfers to our school, and *you* like her?" Claire shot back.

"Not gonna happen. I've lo — liked you for too long. Now that I know you like me, too, I'm, like, all in. I don't want to meet anyone else."

Claire heard the little slip. Dani was *totally* going to say love. Why didn't she? They've said it before. Of course, not as girlfriends, but as best friends. Was it really *that* different? *Yes*, she thought immediately. Saying you love someone romantically is a game-changer. She could understand Dani's hesitation. Though, if she were honest, she loved Dani. Romantically. And she had for a long time.

"Can't it be the same for me?" she asked.

Dani shrugged. "I guess. Look, you're gonna have to cut me some slack here, Claire. I *just* found out you're gay and you like me. My brain is still catching up."

Claire offered Dani a small smile in response. She was right. Even though it was ten years in the making, this relationship stuff was spreading like someone put accelerant on it.

"How about we *both* try to be understanding and talk things out without assuming?"

"I think I can do that. Are you going to stay the night?"

Claire took out her phone and texted her mom. It was all very ordinary and familiar. All except the butterflies in her stomach. She had spent the night with Dani hundreds of times before. But she had never *spent* the night with Dani. She hoped she was ready for this.

"Done."

"Good. Now, can we go back to when you said you've thought about doing *things* with me?"

Chapter Three

"Wanna go make out behind the bleachers?" Dani grinned at Claire as she tossed the paper bag holding her lunch down on the table and settled in next to her.

"Didn't get enough last night?" Claire responded saucily.

They had spent the weekend exploring their newfound relationship. That included *lots* of practice kissing, but that's as far as it went. Both were still a little afraid of taking it to the next step. Each wanted to, yet both were virgins. That "next step" was a huge one. The kissing, though, had gotten better. And hotter. Claire was grateful that Dani's mom worked the graveyard shift. They had *all* night to practice, and it was paying off.

"Did you?"

Claire giggled. "No."

"To the bleachers or getting enough?"

"Both?"

This was their first day back at school since they became a couple. Claire was worried that even if they didn't tell anyone, it would show on her face. Dani had no such worries. She'd had had to learn to school her features quite often when she was around Claire.

"Fair. Are you coming over tonight?"

"I can't. I have to go out to dinner with the fam."

"Oh. 'Kay." Dani unrolled the paper bag and took out a sad looking pb&j.

"Peanut butter and jelly?"

"Um, Mom hasn't gone shopping yet." Dani lifted a shoulder as though it didn't bother her. "She says she's been busy, and if I wanted to go shopping, I could get a job."

"Wow. Is your mom getting worse?"

Before Dani could answer, they both jumped at the loud bang on the table.

"Get up," Noah snarled.

"What?" Dani's cheek bulged from the big bite of her pb&j she just took, but that didn't stop her from looking up at Noah like he had horns. She was pretty sure she could actually see them.

"You heard me, dyke. Get up. I don't want you sitting next to my girlfriend."

"Excuse me?!" Claire exclaimed.

Dani turned to Claire. "Noah? Really?"

"Peer pressure," Claire muttered before turning her ire onto Noah. "How dare you? First, what makes you think you can talk to people like that?"

"I—"

"Second," Claire cut him off. "I am *not* your girlfriend. I canceled our date because I don't like you, Noah."

"Wait," one of Noah's buddies chimed in. "You said you had her on her knees in minutes."

Claire felt Dani bristle beside her and knocked Dani's knee with hers. She wanted to take care of this herself. For ten years, Dani stood up for Claire. Claire had always been too timid to get involved when Dani was being bullied. But not this time.

"Is that what you have to do to make yourself feel like a big boy, Noah? Lie? You're disgusting, and the *only* reason I said yes to a date is because you wouldn't leave me alone. I couldn't do it, though. Just the thought of spending time with you makes me sick."

Noah sneered at her. His face was already red with embarrassment from being caught in a lie. "I *knew* you were a dyke! Just like her!"

A small crowd had begun to form around them. Including Claire's so-called friends. They certainly weren't standing behind her or up for her. To everyone's surprise — including Dani's — Claire smiled.

"You keep saying that word like it means something dirty."

"It does!"

"Why? Because *you* say so? It's been established that you lie."

"It's wrong."

"Says who? You want to call me or Dani dykes, go ahead. I mean, if the shoe fits, we should wear it. But even though you try to say it in a way that makes it sound bad, it's not. Being gay is nothing to be ashamed of. People like you need to catch up. Besides, I've heard that you and your little group there like to look at each other's dicks in the locker room. Are you sure you're straight?"

She could practically see steam coming from Noah's ears. *Oops, did I hit a nerve there?* Her secret smirk faded when he lunged toward her. Before she knew what happened, Dani was there, shielding her.

"Back off, asshole!"

"All this is your fault, you fucking . . ."

"Dyke, yeah, I know. Get some new material."

"Mr. Anderson!" Principal Stevens bellowed. "My office! Now!"

"What about them? They . . ."

"I said now, Mr. Anderson."

"This isn't over," he growled as he stomped off.

"I'm sure it isn't." Claire rolled her eyes. She looked up at her other "friends" and shook her head. "I can see how you feel written all over your faces. If you don't like that I'm with Dani, that's your problem. If you want to be associated with assholes like Noah, also your problem. But don't you dare look at me with pity as though I just ruined my life. If anything, I've finally learned to *live* my life. It's fine if you don't understand that or don't want to be my friend anymore. Because, honestly, I don't want to be *your* friend if you have a problem with my girlfriend."

No one said a word. They merely turned — with what Dani considered shame — and walked away quietly.

"Wow." Dani plopped back down. "Is it corny to say I'm proud of you?"

Claire blushed. "Yes. But thank you."

"Um, Claire?"

Claire swiveled her head and looked up at a girl she knew was a freshman. She recognized her because the girl was always so quiet and reserved. She constantly walked with her head down, her books in front of her like a shield, and fast. Like she was trying to zoom past all the negativity she knew was lurking.

"Hey. Lulu, right?"

The girl blushed profusely. "Y-yeah. I, uh, just wanted to say thank you."

Claire's brows furrowed. "For?"

"Being brave enough to stand up to that guy."

"Oh. Um, Dani does it all the time."

Lulu blushed again when she glanced at Dani. "I know. We

already think she's cool. But you're, um, more like us. Not so open. When you stood up to him, it kinda made us think it wouldn't be so bad being more like Dani."

Claire looked over at Dani, who looked a little uncomfortable. Too bad. She was about to make it worse. Poor Dani.

"It's because of Dani that I was able to. She told me that the only one who could give these bullies power is us. I chose not to give Noah any power over me."

Lulu nodded and gave Dani a shy smile. "I hope to be as brave as you one day."

Dani cleared her throat. "You, um, are. You're standing here right now, telling us who you are. Don't be ashamed of that." She grinned. "Be proud!"

Lulu's smile got a little bigger. A little bolder. "We'll try!"

"Who's we?" Claire called out when Lulu turned to leave.

Lulu shifted awkwardly. "There are a few of us who stick together. Everyone may not know about us, but we know each other. It makes us feel a little less alone." With that, she left Dani and Claire alone.

"Did you know there was a *club*?" Claire asked as she stared after Lulu.

"Wish I did. Maybe I wouldn't have felt so alone."

"Or, I could have told you years ago. I don't feel as brave as Lulu thinks I am."

"Claire, I didn't mean it that way! You should never do something as life-altering as coming out for someone else's benefit. You do it when you're ready."

"Or when it's better that people know you're a lesbian rather than think you're getting down on your knees for someone like Noah."

Dani chuckled. "Or that." She wrapped her half-eaten sandwich up and threw it back in the bag. Maybe she would finish it in World History class if she stayed awake long enough. "You know everyone is going to be talking about this, right?"

"I'm aware," Claire said softly.

"And that your parents may find out?"

Claire looked up sharply. "Why? Your mom still doesn't know."

"Yeah, but no one knows my mom. She doesn't come to any of the school functions. I don't have any other friends. At least none that come to the house. But your mom is pretty active here. She's friends with the other moms. What if your friends say something?"

"Shit," Claire muttered, surprising Dani. Then she shrugged. "Oh well."

"Oh well?"

"Yeah. They're going to have to know eventually. I don't know how they're going to react, but I doubt they'll throw me out."

"Don't ever say you're not brave again. Lulu and her group should strive to be like you, not me. Ready?"

"For my parents to know?"

Dani laughed. "No, for class. Lunch is over."

Claire was glad to be home. Even though she was Dani's ride, she pulled into her own driveway instead of taking Dani home. It was their thing. Claire thought it was because Dani's mom left shortly after they got out of school. The longer it took her to get home, the less Dani had to interact with her mom. The difference was today Dani walked Claire up to her front door and gave her a cute grin before taking off towards her house with a slight pep in her step. Claire had asked on their drive home why Dani was so happy. Dani responded with "'Cuz you're my girlfriend." It was sweet enough for Claire to forget about the day she just had.

But now she was alone, and the day flooded back. Claire may have sounded fearless at lunch, but walking the halls without Dani next to her, she was scared shitless. She saw the looks, heard the whispers. Maybe she was hypersensitive, and it was all in her head. What *wasn't* in her head was how Noah's friends blamed her for his suspension. It didn't matter that he consistently broke the zero-tolerance rules by bullying everyone. Nope. *She* stood up to him, so it was all *her* fault.

"*Whatever*," she muttered grumpily as she walked in the house.

"Did you say something, honey?"

Claire nearly screamed at the sound of her mom's voice. "What are you doing here?"

"I live here." Karen Oliver eyed her daughter. Something was off. Claire was usually upbeat and talkative. Now, however, she merely grunted and walked off towards the stairs. "Claire, are you alright?"

"Yes!" Claire waited until she was close to the top of the stairs before answering. If her mom couldn't see the misery, she couldn't ask about it. She blamed her crappy luck today that her mom was home early. *Oh, shit! What if she knows?* Claire about jumped out of her skin when there was a knock at the door. *Stupid nerves.* Those stupid nerves tripled at the thought that her mom was home because she wanted to talk about Claire's announcement today.

"Claire Bear?" Karen poked her head around the door. "Can I come in?"

Claire rolled her eyes at the juvenile nickname. *That* was for her mom's benefit. Deep down inside, she loved it. Her parents have been calling her that since she was born. It was always said with love and affection. Even now. Maybe her mom didn't know. Yet.

"Yeah."

Karen came in and sat on the bed next to her daughter.

"Want to talk about it?"

"Talk about what?"

"Whatever it is that's making you grumpy."

Claire grinned at her mom. "What are you doing home so early?"

"I had a few errands to run before dinner tonight."

"Errands. Like grocery shopping?" Claire laughed. "You *always* do that, and I haven't figured out why! Every time we schedule a family dinner, you have to go to the grocery store. What's the deal with that?"

"Truth?" Claire nodded, and Karen leaned in conspiratorially. "Your dad wakes up with munchies in the middle of the night. If I don't have something *somewhat* nutritious, there's no telling what he'll concoct."

Claire giggled. "That's because when he eats here, he has, like, three helpings!"

"This is true. Now, do you want to talk about it?"

Sigh. As much as she could have used some of that bravado from earlier, Claire was too exhausted to drum any up.

"There's this boy at school," Claire began.

"Someone you like?"

"Hell no! I, uh, mean heck no. He's terrible. But I agreed to go out with him."

"Your date on Friday that you skipped, with Noah? If he's terrible, why did you say yes?"

"Peer pressure?" Claire shrugged. "I couldn't do it, though. The thought of spending time with him . . ." she shivered and gave an overly dramatic "ew."

"Did he give you problems today for canceling?"

"Kinda. Mom, he told people that I, um, did things to him. And I didn't even go out with him! But they all believed him."

Karen jumped up. "Oh, I am going to have a talk with his mother! How dare he . . ."

"Mom! No! I took care of it. Besides, he's suspended. I don't think there's anything more you can do."

"I can make sure he's expelled!" Karen was fired up. *No one* talked about her baby girl like that. Damn, privileged, little prick! She didn't care for his mom, either. That woman thought she was queen of the PTA. Typical, entitled, Botox-faced . . .

"Mom?"

"Bitch."

"Huh?"

"Oh! Not you, Claire Bear. I was thinking about that dumbass's mom. That rotten apple didn't fall far from the tree."

"Why don't you tell me how you really feel?" Claire laughed. She didn't see her mom get riled up often, but when she did, it was hysterical.

"At least you're laughing," Karen smiled and sat back down. "Is there anything else?"

Claire's heart skipped a beat. *Just tell her!* "No. I mean, all his friends — and those I thought were *my* friends — are blaming me for him getting in trouble. But it's fine."

"If they're blaming everyone except the one responsible, they weren't your friends anyway. What does Dani say about all this?"

Another beat skipped. "She stood up for me. Like, literally. I said something to Noah that made him mad, and he made a move." Claire grabbed her mom's arm before she could stand again. "Don't worry, Dani was there to protect me."

"She's a good kid." Karen took a steadying breath. This Noah kid sounded more and more like a psycho. Regardless of what Claire said, Karen thought a visit to his mother was a good idea. Or maybe the authorities.

"Whatever you're plotting, please don't."

"The great thing about being a mom is I don't have to listen to you." She stuck her tongue out at Claire. "I will do what I believe is right to protect you, Claire. But enough of that for now. We have a dinner to get ready for. Do you feel a little better?"

"Yeah." Claire stood with her mom and hugged her. She wished Dani had this. "Hey, mom? Could Dani come with us tonight? Her mom is working, and they don't have much to eat in the house."

"Of course! Are they having financial troubles?"

Claire shrugged. "I don't know. Dani's kinda quiet when it

comes to all that. All she'll say is her mom hasn't been the same since, you know."

"I know. Losing a husband and father is devastating. If Dani or Rita needs anything, including groceries, let us know, okay? We're happy to help."

"Thanks, mom. I'm gonna call Dani. She's going to be annoyed with me."

"For asking her to dinner?"

"For not doing it before she walked all the way home!"

"Mom!" The car wasn't here, so she knew her mom had to have left already. She still called out to make sure. The car was iffy at best. Dani didn't trust that it wouldn't break down, and her mom would be stranded at home. "Damn car. If Dad were here, he'd make sure it was running just fine."

She shook off the wave of depression she always got when thinking of her dad. Her mom didn't care. About the car, the house, the groceries . . . about Dani. Dani opened a cupboard, found nothing worth putting in her belly in there, then continued her search. She found some crackers, some questionable meat in the freezer, and a couple of potatoes that looked like they were sprouting baby potatoes.

"Maybe I should get a job." Even if she could scrounge up a few bucks for some fast food, she had no way of getting there. Claire was going out with her family, and she and her mom only had one car. "Ooo, maybe Claire will let me borrow her car. She won't need it."

She brought out her phone and bobbled it when it began buzzing. She juggled it for a while, giving herself a virtual pat on the back when she caught it before dropping it.

"Yeah, hello?"

"Why do you sound out of breath?"

"Because you just scared the crap outta me! I was just about to call you when you freakin' made my phone scream at me!"

"It is not my fault that you have that stupid ring tone. Which is insulting to me, by the way."

Dani snickered. Claire loved Taylor Swift. Dani . . . not so much. When she made Claire's ringtone a screaming goat, it was not appreciated. Funny as hell, but not appreciated.

"Still not changing it."

"Not even for your girlfriend?" Claire asked sweetly.

"Um . . . well, maybe. I thought you were going to dinner."

"I am. I called to invite you."

"Huh?" Family dinner was just that. Family only. Not once in the ten plus years they'd known each other had Dani ever been invited.

"I'm inviting you to dinner, Dani."

"Why?"

"What do you mean, why?"

"Do they know about us," Dani asked cautiously.

Claire hesitated. She hoped Dani wouldn't think she was a wuss. "Uh, no. I told Mom about Noah and what he told others I did to him. And I told her you protected me."

Claire's voice was so soft Dani almost didn't hear her. "Why would you say that? You didn't need my protection. You put that douchecanoe in his place all on your own."

"Douchecanoe? That's a new one. I'll have to write that one down."

"You joke, but it's a good one."

"Mmhmm. Anyway, do you want to come to dinner?"

Dani looked at her poor excuse for dinner, then remembered why she had her phone in her hand in the first place. "Oh, um, yeah. Actually, the reason I was about to call you was to ask if I could borrow your car. And maybe a couple of bucks. Guess I don't need to now if I'm going to dinner with you."

"Well, get your cute butt over here then. We leave in like twenty minutes."

Claire hung up, and Dani stared into space for a moment. "She said I had a cute butt! Ha!" She wiggled said butt and did a little happy dance. "Shit! I need to change!"

"How is your mom doing, Dani?" Karen's attention was focused on Dani and missed Claire's warning look.

"She's, um, okay, I guess. Working a lot."

"Things must be difficult after such a tragic loss."

"Mom, maybe Dani doesn't want to talk about this and just enjoy her dinner."

"Nah, it's okay, Claire. It is. We don't talk much. Then again, we don't see each other very often with her schedule."

"You know, if you ever need anything, we're here."

Dani slid a glance over at Claire, who had the grace to blush. She couldn't be mad at Claire for wanting to help. On the other hand, Dani hated that Claire's mom was now worried about her and knew her business.

"I, uh, I know, Momma K. It's all good. Just trying to find our way after dad, ya know?"

"I know, sweetie. You are welcome to come have dinner with us while your mom is working."

"Oh. I don't wanna wear out my welcome."

"You won't," Claire cut in. "I think it's a great idea! Do you know what else is a great idea, *Mom*? Changing the topic."

"Alright, alright. I can take a hint."

"Shocking," Claire mumbled playfully and received a dinner roll in the face for it.

Dani chuckled, her discomfort at being the center of attention fading. As much as she hated talking about herself or being seen as "needy" in any way, she was grateful for Momma Karen's generosity. It made Dani feel a little less alone in the world. First Claire, now this. Things were starting to look up for the first time since her dad's death.

"Sorry about my mom," Claire said quietly.

They were sitting out on the front porch, enjoying the cool evening. The rest of the dinner had been uneventful, and yet fun. Normal. Dani missed normal.

"It's okay. Your mom is just trying to help."

"Yeah, I know. I didn't want you to think I was betraying your confidence. I worry about you."

Dani bumped Claire's shoulder. "Don't worry about me. It's all good."

"Really? What were you going to eat tonight if we hadn't invited you to dinner?"

Dani thought about the crackers, frozen meat, and sprouting potatoes. "Um, I was going to get a taco or something."

"How?"

"Come on, Claire."

"I'm just saying, Dani. I have reason to worry about you. So does Mom. Let us. God knows your mom doesn't."

"Fine. But I'm not a charity case. If I eat here, I do chores here."

Claire laughed. "Mom will never go for that."

"Too bad. She'll have to. I'll clean out the garage or something."

"*Dad* would never go for that." Claire stood up and put her hands on her hips. "Everything has its place, Claire Bear!" she said, mimicking her father's booming voice.

Dani fell backward on the porch, clutching her stomach as she laughed hysterically. "You sound *just* like him!"

Claire sat back down next to Dani. "Mom thinks of you as one of her kids. You don't have to work for your food."

"That's gross, Claire."

"What?"

"We're *dating*," she whispered dramatically. "I don't want to be thought of as your sister!"

Claire rolled her eyes. "You know, if we got married, you'd be Mom's daughter, too. It doesn't have to be a sister thing."

"M-married?"

Claire giggled. "You're such a weirdo. Calm down. I wasn't asking you to marry me. I was explaining the differences . . ."

"*I would.*"

"What?"

Dani shrugged. "I would. I mean, it's not like I haven't thought about our future. In all my dreams, you were there with me. I could never imagine my life without you. Before I knew you were into me, I didn't know how it would work, but now? Maybe now the future is a little less fuzzy."

"You're serious?"

"Yeah, I am."

"You're such a weirdo!" Claire laughed. She discreetly brushed Dani's finger with hers. "I would, too."

Chapter Four

"Dani! Get your ass in here!"

Dani groaned and wrapped her pillow around her head to try and drown out her mother's grating voice. It was Saturday morning. A day to sleep in. A day to do nothing but stay in her boxers and play video games at least until Claire was ready to do something.

"Dani!"

"What!"

"Get in here, now!"

Dani took a moment to have a little tantrum, kicking the bed and screaming into her pillow, before throwing the covers off and stomping out of her room.

"What?"

"Don't talk to me like that. I am your mother."

You sure don't act like it. "Well, it was obviously important that I get out here right away. I'm here."

Rita whipped open the refrigerator door. "What the hell is this?"

The fridge was stocked full of food — courtesy of the Olivers.

"Food? Or is there something specific you don't recognize?"

Her mom slammed the door shut. It took her less than a second to get to Dani and slap her hard across the face. She was awake now.

"What the hell!" It was the first time either of her parents had ever hit her. Even when she was little and a bit brattier than other toddlers her age, they never hit her. They never spanked her. After the slap, Dani could positively say she didn't like it.

"I told you not to talk to me like that. Where did you get the groceries? Did you steal them?"

Dani scoffed. "No, I didn't *steal* them." She was still rubbing her stinging cheek. "Claire's mom took me shopping."

"You told them we needed food? We are *not* a charity case!"

Now I know where I get it. "They don't think that. They're just trying to help out. Ever since Dad died, it's been rough. There was no food in the house, and you're always working. I don't have a car to get a job. They offered, I said okay. I thought I was doing something good for us."

"You thought wrong. Take it back."

"To the store? Are you crazy?" Dani ducked when her mom lashed out at her again.

"Take it back to those self-righteous pricks."

"They're not self-righteous. And I can't just take it back to them. It's rude."

"Rude is thinking they're better than us!"

"They don't think that! When Dad died, people brought us food all the time. What's different now?"

Rita went back to the fridge and jerked the door open again. "Organic shit. Fruits, vegetables, expensive meat. All they're doing is rubbing it in our face how rich they are."

"They're not rich," Dani muttered. It was a stupid retort, but it was all she had. She was completely confused by her mom's reaction to something so nice. "It's food, ma. Not a big deal."

"Next time they want to flaunt their shit in our faces, you better refuse. We don't need anyone's help."

"Yeah, sure. Can I go now?" Dani took her mom's silence as a yes and hightailed it out of there. It took her four minutes and thirty-eight seconds to get dressed, brush her teeth and hair, and get out of the house. She thought about going to her pier, but it was a long walk. She also forgot her TAP card so she couldn't catch the bus. So she went to the one person who always made her feel better. Claire.

"I'll get it," Claire announced to the table when the doorbell rang. "Don't eat my waffles, Dad."

"No promises." Jose Oliver deliberately reached over and stole a bite of his daughter's food.

"Mom! Keep him away from my food!" Claire was still laughing when she opened the door and saw Dani standing there. "Hey! You're up early. We were just having breakfast."

"Sorry. I'll . . ."

"Dani! Where are you going? Get in here, silly!"

"Nah, I don't want to interrupt."

"Dani? Look at me?" Claire stepped out on the porch and looked closely at her girlfriend. "What's wrong? Why is your cheek red?"

She was going to lie. It was on her tongue to lie. But the look of concern on Claire's face had that lie dissolving into the absolute truth.

"Mom slapped me."

"What! Why?" Claire touched Dani's cheek tenderly. If

they hadn't been standing there in front of the opened front door, she would have kissed it.

"Because I accepted groceries from you guys."

Claire's hand dropped heavily to her side out of sheer disbelief. She knew Dani's mom could be difficult, but to hit her because she accepted help? That was too much. "Are you fucking kidding me?"

"Claire! Watch your mouth, your parents might hear."

"I don't care. Why would she hit you for that? And don't shrug!"

Dani was about to do just that. "She's stressed out, I guess."

"That doesn't excuse her for hitting you."

"It was just a slap."

"Ugh. Come on." Claire grabbed Dani's hand and pulled her inside. "Mom, Dani's here!" she called out before they got to the kitchen. Once they got there, Karen was already setting another place at the table.

"Thanks, Momma K. Mornin', Pops."

Jose smiled at Dani. "Morning. I didn't think you were up this early on the weekends. You didn't come to clean my garage, did you?"

Dani chuckled. "No, sir. I've been warned."

"Are you feeling okay? You seem flushed." Karen touched Dani's forehead with the back of her hand.

The motherly gesture nearly made Dani cry. "Nah, I'm good. I ran over here."

"Dani, tell them."

Dani gave Claire a look, but it didn't faze her, and Dani sighed with resignation. "So, um, Mom wasn't too happy about the groceries."

Karen paused in the act of filling Dani's plate with food. "Why?"

"She thinks you see us as a charity case," Dani admitted softly. She was embarrassed even to say the words out loud.

"That's not why I took you shopping, sweetie."

"Oh, I know. And I tried to tell her that. I think she's tired and stressed. I wouldn't worry about it too much."

"I would," Claire chimed in bitingly. "She hit Dani!"

"Claire, stop making it so dramatic. I got mouthy with her, and she slapped me. It's not a big deal."

Karen glanced at her husband. She was afraid something like this would happen between Rita and Dani. Their relationship had been strained before Dani's father, Kenneth, passed away. When the glue disappears from the family, it's only a matter of time before things start to fall apart.

"Maybe you should stay here for a while. You know, give you and your mom a little break from each other? I think it would help things."

Dani thought about it but decided it was a terrible idea. She and Claire were getting a bit more hot and heavy with each other during their make-out sessions. Dani couldn't think about doing that while living under Karen and Jose's roof. Their setup now was perfect. Claire would spend a couple of nights a week over at Dani's house while Rita was at work. Other nights, at least this past week, Dani would have dinner with the Olivers and then head home alone. Those nights, she still slept with Claire. Only on the phone.

"Thank you for the invitation, but I think I should stay put. Mom and I may not get along, but I can't just leave her there alone."

"Dani, I don't . . ."

"Karen, my love," Jose interrupted gently. He knew his wife wanted to fix everything. Sometimes things needed to work themselves out. If things got worse between Rita and Dani, Jose would step in. But he had a feeling the youngster needed to decide this on her own terms. "Dani, you always have a place here if you need it. We trust you know what's best for you. However, if we hear that things have gotten worse from someone other than you, we will step in. I don't want to see you get hurt. Understand?"

"Yes, sir."

"Are you mad at me?"

Claire sat in the passenger seat of her car, opting to let Dani drive since she knew where she was going.

"For tattling on me?"

"I did not *tattle* on you, Dani Reed. I don't want you to have to go through —" She stopped mid-tirade when she saw Dani laughing. "You're not nice."

"I'm *very* nice! I'm taking you to my special place."

Claire giggled. "That sounds dirty!"

Dani nearly swerved off the road. "Claire! You have a filthy mind."

"Ha! Like you can talk. Half of the things I say lately, you're turning it into some innuendo."

It was true, Dani couldn't deny it. They both had said they

weren't ready for the next step yet, but Dani was definitely getting there. If Claire's responses the last few make-out sessions were any indication, she was getting there, too. Just the thought of sex with Claire made Dani's nerves stand on end. But she wanted to make sure she wasn't just thinking with her, ahem, hooha. She wanted both her and Claire's hearts and heads involved *if* the sex were to happen between them.

"Dani?"

"Huh?"

"I asked how far this place is." Claire couldn't help but wonder if Dani's thoughts were on par with her own. Sex. It was a scary thing to think about. She knew some of her friends — former friends — had already done it. But Claire didn't trust them to tell the truth about how it made them feel. They weren't doing it with someone they had loved for, like, ever. Claire would be. She didn't know if that made it better or worse. She also didn't know how much longer she could *just* kiss. *Maybe we could try touching a little.*

"Are you listening?"

Claire looked over at Dani and blinked. "Uh, no."

Dani laughed until she snorted. "I said I missed the turn. I guess we have other things on our mind." She glanced over at Claire and was delighted by the slight blush that confirmed her suspicions. They were thinking about the same thing.

After another ten minutes of circling back, they finally made it to their destination. Dani turned off the engine and sat there quietly, letting Claire take it all in. She was glad it was a lovely day today. The sun was out, clouds were scarce, and the air was cool but not too cold to be near the water. Dani would like to think her dad had something to do with it being perfect for Claire.

"What is this place?"

"An abandoned part of the beach. If you go up or down about two miles, there are a bunch of people because that's where all the shops and stuff are. I think it's kinda cool that this part is, like, forgotten about."

"It says no trespassing," Claire said as she got out of the car.

"Yeah, but there's an old dude that cleans up around here. I help him sometimes, so he lets me come out here when I need to. He says that if anyone says anything to me, tell them to take it up with him."

"I feel like there's a part of your life I have no clue about."

Dani took off her shoes and motioned for Claire to do the same. "This is it, Claire. This is the only thing I've kept from you until now. I mean, if you don't, like, count the being in love with you stuff."

Claire froze. "You said it."

"What?"

"You said the "L" word!"

Dani scoffed. "I said I'd marry you, too. I thought those two things went together. Like pasta and alfredo sauce."

Claire scrunched her nose. "Spaghetti sauce."

Dani shrugged. "You say potato, I say alfredo." She laughed and sang it again and again. She was feeling pretty good about herself and her little joke.

"Are you done being a weirdo?"

"Nope!" Dani winked at her girlfriend and grabbed her hand. "Come on. I'll introduce you to Craberton the Third. You two should get along swimmingly." She guffawed again at her cleverness. She was on a *roll*!

Claire fought hard to maintain her stern face, but Dani's enthusiasm was too contagious. And, after the morning Dani had with her mother, Claire was glad to see her so happy. That burden-free happiness was rare these days.

"I'm sure Craberton the Third is a gentleman," Claire laughed.

"Most of the time. Sometimes he can be a little crabby, though."

Claire shook her head. "I like seeing you like this. it's been a while."

Dani stopped howling with laughter long enough to acknowledge Claire's statement. "It's because of you, ya know. Life is just easier knowing you're here with me. I mean, I know you were before, but it's different now that you're my girlfriend. It makes me feel, I don't know, free or something."

"Dani Reed. You are a romantic!" Claire linked her fingers with Dani's. Their arms swung between them. "I love you, too, by the way."

The smile on Dani's face could light the entire city.

Claire dug her fingers into the wet sand and scooped up a big handful.

"Why do you like coming here?" she asked Dani as she sifted through her pile of sand.

Dani watched Claire with amusement. "I dunno. It's quiet and imperfect, I guess. Kinda like me."

Claire glanced over at Dani. It was on the tip of her tongue to say "you are perfect" to Dani but knew it would have been the wrong response. The one thing she *knew* about Dani was that placating her was worse than just telling her the truth. And while Claire loved Dani, being perfect didn't describe either one of them.

"Imperfect or not, it's beautiful." She knew she said something good when Dani beamed at her.

"What are you doing?" Dani asked when Claire went for another handful of wet sand.

"Looking for treasure."

Dani snorted. "I think the only thing you're gonna find is a crabby Craberton the Third for demolishing his house."

"Whatever," Claire laughed. "I'm not demolishing. I'm renovating." She put the sand back where she found it and patted it smooth again. "See? Better than before."

Dani shook her head. "Did you find any treasures?"

"Yep! Look!" Claire held out her hand, showing off her findings. They were tiny little shells. Some white, some purple, some yellow. All very important to her because of where they were found. Claire would keep them forever, remembering the day Dani shared something so private with her.

"Very pretty!" *The shells are nice, too.* Dani cleared her throat and looked out at the ocean. She needed the distraction, or she would have kissed Claire right then and there. While the place was secluded, she wasn't sure Claire would have appreciated the PDA.

"What do you think about when you're out here?" Claire

asked. She had wanted Dani to kiss her. To be honest, she wanted Dani to do more than that out here. Maybe it was the sound of the waves. Or perhaps it was feeling like only the two of them existed at the moment. Whatever it was, Claire thought it was best to change the subject.

Dani lifted a shoulder. "All kinds of things. And nothing. It depends on my mood."

"What about the last time you were here?"

Ugh. The day I thought you had a date. "Um, my heart was broken. I don't think I had great thoughts that day. I did talk to Dad, though."

Since she and Dani had been spending every spare minute together lately, Claire assumed the last time Dani was here was when she found out about the stupid date. "I didn't mean to hurt you, Dani."

"No, I know. It's all good now. But at the time, I was contemplating enlisting."

Claire stopped her treasure hunting and stared at Dani. "In the Army?"

"Yeah. Maybe the Air Force, though. Pilots are cool, right?"

"Wait, are you still thinking about it?"

"No," Dani laughed. "Unless you decide you can't be dating a high-schooler when you're in college." She was joking. Kinda.

"Oh, you're not getting rid of me that easy." She side-eyed Dani. "I can't see you in the military."

Dani frowned. "Why? Too dyke-y?"

Claire rolled her eyes. "No. You don't like authority. Or discipline. Or getting up early. Or . . ."

"Alright, I get it. Geesh. I'm a lazy, unruly bum."

Claire giggled. "I didn't say that. I just meant you have your own way of doing things. You like doing things outside the box. The military seems very . . . boxed in."

"I suppose. I mean, I don't really want to enlist. I just wanted to get away, ya know? Don't you ever want to pack a bag and just *go*?"

"Not really," Claire confessed. "I love living here. My family is here, and *you're* here. Traveling is nice, but I'd always want to come home." It scared her to think Dani was restless. Did she need more out of life than just Claire?

"Before you told me you *liked* me, I thought about taking off. Especially after Dad died and left me alone with Mom. The military was just one idea. Backpacking across Europe was another. See the world and explore, ya know?"

"Being with me changes that?" Claire asked carefully. She didn't want to be the one who held Dani back from her dreams. She also didn't want to lose her best friend.

"Yeah, of course."

"Why?"

"What do you mean? It changes that because I have someone here who loves me again, Claire. Now the only adventures I want to go on are with you."

I've always loved you. Tears welled up in Claire's eyes. "I hope I never disappoint you."

Dani put her arm around Claire and pulled her close. "I hope I never disappoint *you*. I know this is our first — and only — relationship, and it's all shiny and new. But I'm not dumb, Claire. Relationships are hard, and there's always a chance we won't last. I prefer to believe we will. What's that saying? The future is what we make it?"

Claire laughed. "I think you're quoting Back to the Future."

"Nuh-uh. It was some old philosopher guy that we learned about, wasn't it?"

"Nope. I'm pretty sure it was Doc Brown. You should know, you watch that movie every time it's on."

"Oh. Well, whatever. It still applies."

"How about we start with the very near future," Claire suggested. "I think I'm ready to go home. With you."

Chapter Five

"You didn't have to make it sound like you were staying with me to babysit me," Dani groused.

"I didn't, but I'm allowed to worry about you. Besides, what did you want me to say? 'Hey Mom, I'm going to stay over at Dani's tonight and contemplate losing my virginity to her. 'Kay, bye!'"

"I don't know, I . . . what?" Dani tripped over something. Her feet? Her tongue? Who the hell knew? Maybe she tripped over Claire's words. Whatever the hell it was, she found herself on the floor.

"Are you okay?" Claire tried her hardest not to laugh. Unfortunately, she was losing that battle as she tried to help her girlfriend up off the floor.

"No! I'm not getting up until you repeat what you just said. Cuz, if you say what I think you said again, I'll end up right back down here."

Claire shook her head and sat down on the floor with Dani. "Did I freak you out?"

"Did you say," Dani gulped, "that you wanted to lose your virginity with me tonight?"

"Technically, I said I was going to *contemplate* it."

"You and your big words." Dani leaned back against the wall and tried to catch her breath. Her heart was beating so fast she wondered if it was possible for it to explode. God, she hoped not. At least not until *after* maybe, possibly losing *her* virginity, too.

Claire chuckled. "It's not a big word, Dani. It just means I'm seriously thinking about it."

"I thought you weren't ready." *Will you shut up? Don't talk her out of it!*

"I wasn't."

"But now you are?"

Claire sighed and scooted closer to Dani. "I don't know. All I know is when I'm with you; I want more. What that more is, is still a mystery. I could tell you yes right now and then change my mind when we're getting close. I would hope you wouldn't hate me for that."

"Hell no!" Dani turned to face Claire. "I would never pressure you, Claire. Even if we're, like, in the *middle* of, um, *it*, and you changed your mind, I'm going to stop right away. I respect you and love you too much to hurt you."

Claire laid her head on Dani's shoulder. "I wish I had been brave enough to tell you a long time ago that I loved you."

"Nah, you did it right, Claire." Dani kissed her lightly on top of the head. "You weren't ready before now. And, honestly, with everything going on with Dad, I wasn't either. I think we're both in the place we need to be right now."

"Well, it might be a little more comfortable on an actual bed than on the floor in front of your bedroom," Claire teased.

Dani snorted with laughter and hopped up. "M'lady." She bowed and held her hand out to Claire.

"Thank you." Claire squealed slightly when Dani pulled her into her arms.

"Before we go in there," Dani began. "Remember one thing for me, okay?"

"Okay."

"If I do anything that makes you feel uncomfortable or you're not ready for something, tell me. Stop me."

You're making it hard to feel anything but *ready.* "I will if you will."

"Right there! No, go back, go back!"

"Where?"

"Right there! A little to the left. A little more. A little more. Now! You're right on it, Claire!"

"I don't see it!"

"You don't have to see it. It'll vibrate when you're on it."

"Oh! I felt it! Okay, hang on. Okay, I'm on it! Now what?"

"Get it!"

"How?"

"Push this, right there! Yes! You got it!"

Claire flopped back onto the bed, exhausted. "This is too stressful. How do you do this every day?"

"I don't do it *every* day," Dani laughed.

Claire rolled her head towards Dani. "Really?"

"Fine. I do. But it's fun!"

"Fun. I wonder what my heart rate is right now." Claire put two fingers over her carotid artery and counted silently.

"Oh stop! Is this why you never play with me? It's too *hard* for you?"

"Nooo. It's just not my thing," Claire answered with as

much dignity as she could muster in a prone position, practically panting.

"So why did you do it now?"

"Because I love you, and I wanted to understand what all the fuss was about."

"But you don't get it, do you?"

"Nope. But I'll do it again if it's something you really want."

Dani laughed and took the game controller out of Claire's hand. "No, I won't put you through that again. Fortnite is something you either get or you don't. It's fine, babe. We don't have to like all of the same things."

"Whoa, whoa, whoa." Claire caught Dani's arm before she rolled off the bed. "Did you just call me babe?"

"Maybe. If you liked it, then yes. If not, I don't know what's wrong with your ears."

Claire laughed with more energy than she thought she had. "I liked it," she said after she caught her breath.

Dani grinned. "Good. Cuz I totally said it. And I'll probably repeat it. Except at school. Unless we're alone."

She made a silly face, causing Claire to laugh again. From the corner of her eye, she noted the time — 10:35 pm. Her mom had left more than an hour ago after a brief exchange between her and Claire. *That* was something she wished she could have avoided. Claire, of course, was kind and respectful even though she was still pissed about what had happened that morning. Rita, on the other hand, made it known that she and Dani didn't need any help. Claire had to promise to tell her parents that before Rita would let it go. Now it was time for Dani to let it go and focus on the here and now.

Dani stood to put the controllers back on their chargers. "Hey, you wanna take a shower?"

Claire froze. Just as her heart rate had begun to settle, Dani went and spiked it again. "Um, what?" she squeaked.

Dani looked over at Claire curiously. "Shower?" Then she realized how that sounded. "Oh! No! I didn't mean *together*! I meant, do *you* want to take a shower. Alone. And then *I'll* take a shower. Alone. Separately."

Claire blew out a breath of relief. She may have been ready for *some* things, but a *naked* shower with Dani wasn't one of them. *Naked shower*. Claire laughed at herself.

"What?" Dani inquired.

"Nothing. I was just thinking that I'm not ready for a naked shower yet."

"Naked shower?" Dani laughed, too. "Well, in your defense, that's usually how they work." She grabbed a couple of towels from the laundry basket, sniffing them to make sure they were the clean ones. "Here. You can go first."

"Thanks."

Dani plopped herself on her bed, prepared to wait patiently as Claire took her shower. Then something Claire said hit her like a ton of bricks. "Yet??"

She heard the amused giggle from behind the bathroom door.

They laid in bed, stiff as boards. Neither was willing to move an inch for fear of touching the other inadvertently. Describing it as awkward was putting a positive spin on it. They had been so sure this was what they wanted until the time actually arrived. They still wanted to be together, of course. The problem was, neither knew how to . . . start.

This is ridiculous, Dani thought miserably. Her nerves began to fray as soon as Claire got out of the shower wearing only a towel. Apparently, she had forgotten her PJs before going into the bathroom. Dani barely took the time to listen to Claire's explanation as she grabbed her towel, her boxers and t-shirt, and hightailed it out of the room. She had heard about cold showers before, so she tried it. It didn't work. Her libido was working overtime.

It had been an innocent, honest mistake. Claire had been so distracted by Dani's suggestion of a shower that she forgot to take her clothes with her. She didn't take into account how it would affect either of them when she walked out practically naked. *Naked showers*, she rolled her eyes in the dark. If they were both ready, why were they acting so weird? One of them was going to have to make the first move. Should it be her? Should she wait for Dani? What if Dani changed her mind? Was it supposed to be this hard?

"Claire?"

Claire jumped even though Dani's voice was soft. "Yeah?"

"Why are we being weird?"

Claire laughed and turned on her side to face Dani. "I have no idea! It's not like we haven't been on this bed before, making out."

Dani turned, too. "Yeah, but I guess now there's a possibility of more, and that's making us . . ." she made a crazy face causing Claire to laugh again.

"I don't want us to feel uncomfortable with each other, Dani."

"Me either. But I'm so nervous I might need another shower soon."

Claire giggled. She leaned over and kissed Dani lightly on the lips. *That was easy and comfortable.* She tried it again, allowing herself to linger a bit longer.

Dani scooted closer, gingerly putting her hand on Claire's hip. "Remember what I said," she whispered against Claire's lips.

"I do."

They continued to kiss, scooting closer and closer until Dani was practically on top of Claire. As the kisses deepened, there was a thrilling feeling of excitement that eclipsed every other time they had made out. Dani's hand had moved of its own volition, but only to Claire's tummy. She couldn't move it up. She couldn't move it down. It was just stuck in limbo. At this rate, they were both going to be virgins for the rest of their lives.

Claire knew Dani well enough to understand she was having an internal war with herself. Dani was very good at talking herself out of something when it wasn't black-or-white. In her head, Dani was wondering if she was doing the right thing. She was wondering if she was pressuring Claire. That thought alone was most likely what was paralyzing Dani right now. It was up to Claire to reassure Dani. She took Dani's hand and moved it. Down.

"Don't go inside," Claire whispered. "Not yet."

Dani nodded before her mind went completely blank.

"Stop yawning," Claire yawned. They had decided before they fell asleep to be up and out of the house before Dani's mom got home from work. Unfortunately, that meant it was too damn early to be up after such a long night. A long, *beautiful* night.

"Sorry." Dani chuckled at her girlfriend. Damn, she was in a good mood. Exhausted, but happy as hell. Last night had been . . . she didn't even know how to describe it. Losing her virginity to Claire had to have been the best decision she had ever made or would ever make again. Claire granting Dani her virginity was and would always be the most incredible gift she could ever receive. She only wished they could have stayed in bed all morning doing what they did over and over again.

"You're doing it again."

"I didn't yawn!" Dani laughed.

"No, but you're grinning like a fool," Claire teased. "Keep doing that, and everyone will know what we did last night as soon as we walk in my house."

Dani stopped and took Claire's arm, effectively stopping her, too. "About that," she began.

"Dani Reed, do not ask me again if I'm okay with everything that happened."

"I just want to make sure, Claire."

"You've asked me, like, twenty times already. And every time, what have I answered?"

"Yes," Dani responded sheepishly.

"And?"

"And that you enjoyed it very much and can't wait to do it one hundred thousand more times."

Claire laughed. "You're paraphrasing, but that's basically it."

Dani grinned a toothy grin. "I enjoyed it, too. A lot."

"I'm glad." This time, Claire stopped Dani when she started walking again. "I mean that, Dani. I'm glad it was you. I'm glad it *is* you."

"Me, too," Dani said sincerely. "Now, wipe that silly smile off your face before someone figures out what we did." She stuck her tongue out at Claire and took off running.

The squeal of tires so early in the morning startled Claire enough to give Dani a head start. But she was athletic enough to catch up with her girlfriend. Plus, she was *starving*. She wondered if it was too early for her mom to be up and cooking something tasty and filling. If it was, she was raiding all the cereal boxes.

CHAPTER SIX

Who knew that losing your virginity to someone you loved would completely change how you felt about yourself? Most people who met Claire Oliver would believe she was a confident person. She was intelligent, pretty, and kind. But growing up knowing you felt different than what others would describe as normal, Claire's confidence was low. Until the day she was honest with Dani. Every day she spent with Dani, Claire's courage grew. After they made love for the first time — was that really just a week ago — Claire walked a little taller. She held her head a little higher. And, best of all, she loved *herself* a little more.

Claire was learning that it wasn't her virginity that held her back. And it wasn't losing it that incited the changes. This feeling wasn't that superficial. It was Dani. It was how Dani treated Claire. How confident Dani was of *who* she is and what she felt for Claire. How she didn't placate Claire or make empty promises. *That* was why Claire had changed. She didn't care if anyone thought they were too young to be in love. She knew what she felt for Dani — and vice versa — was real. Each time they were together, that became more apparent.

"Hey, Claire?"

Claire turned to see one of her fake friends walking towards her. She rolled her eyes at the overly dramatic makeup and "look-how-rich-I-wish-I-was" designer clothes.

"Bristol." *Ugh.* Even saying her name made Claire's skin crawl. How could she ever have thought they were friends?

"Did you hear?"

"I hear a lot of things," Claire responded with disinterest and continued walking to class. She picked up her pace when Bristol followed along. If the girl wanted to talk to Claire, she was going to have to work for it.

"Noah is back."

Claire stopped, turned, and walked the opposite way briskly. Class was forgotten. All she knew was she had to find Dani and make sure she was okay.

Dani was whistling as she walked to class. She couldn't get rid of the stupid grin on her face, and she didn't even care. Nor did she care if others thought she was crazy. She was. Crazy in love. Eff the people who thought she was too young to know what love was. There was no freakin' way that what she felt when she was with Claire wasn't pure love. Dani hadn't felt safe or loved since her dad died. She had lived in fear of what she would do when Claire found a boyfriend. Now she lived with anticipation for the next time she could see her girlfriend. The next time she could kiss her. Or make love to her. Dani's grin widened after that thought. They hadn't done it one-hundred thousand more times, yet, but they also weren't wasting any time trying to get to that number. It had only been a week since their first time, and they've already been together, like, five more times.

Dani could definitely get used to spending the rest of her life with Claire. She wondered if that feeling she got — the twisting of the belly, the jump of the pulse, the need, and want — would go away eventually. Perhaps it would. But for now, she was going to appreciate it with her whole heart. Did Claire feel the same way? Dani was almost sure she did. She was always as eager as Dani was to be alone. Of course, they had to play it kinda cool at school. They would use either studying or Dani's problems with her mom as cover stories as to why they were spending so much time together. *All worth it.*

"What's with the stupid look, Dyke?"

Dani's good mood deflated a little. Noah was back. *Fantastic.* "It's called being happy, Noah. You should try it sometime."

Dani mentally patted herself on the back. Claire was going to be proud of her! She didn't grab her crotch or use words that Claire didn't approve of. Nope. Dani was cordial-ish.

"Fuck you, Dyke."

"You wish."

"What did you say?" Noah got up in Dani's face, invading her personal space.

"Get out of my way." Dani did her best to remain calm. She certainly wasn't going to show Noah any fear — even if she *was* a little scared.

"Tell me what you said, Dyke. Did you say you wanted me?" Noah raised his voice. "Did you say you've been dreaming about my dick?"

"I'm a dyke, remember? Dyke equals no dick. Ever. Though I will give you one thing. You have some balls coming back from being suspended and starting up right where you left off."

"I got in major shit with my parents for that, bitch."

"Ooh, a new name!"

Noah inched closer. "I'm going to . . ."

"Do we have a problem here, Mr. Anderson?"

Noah smiled, though it looked more like a sneer. "No, sir, Mr. Stevens. Just saying hi to some friends."

"Is that right, Miss Reed?"

Mr. Stevens looked to Dani for confirmation. She had a choice. Get Noah suspended again or suck it up and move on.

"Yes, sir."

Their principal nodded, unconvinced. "Get to class."

"This ain't over," Noah warned.

"I'm sure it isn't since I'll always be a dyke and you'll always be a dick."

"Dani?"

Dani cringed. Of course, Claire would hear *that*. "*Damn it!* I was good, Claire! I swear! I didn't grab my crotch or nothing."

Claire smiled. "I wouldn't care if you did. What did he say to you?"

"Nothing." Dani sighed when Claire just stared at her. "Nothing different. Is that better? Dyke this, dyke that. Oh, wait, he did call me a bitch this time. That's new."

Claire shook her head. "He just got back, and he starts back up again."

"That's what I said!" Dani gave Claire a proud grin. They must really be on the same wavelength if they're thinking the same thing. "Anyway, even after I covered for him, he was still salty."

"You covered for him? Why?"

"Why make things worse? He already hates me." Dani shrugged. "I've been feeling way too good these past few days that I was just tryna keep it going."

Butterflies fluttered around in Claire's stomach, and she gave Dani a brilliant smile. "I, um, guess we should get to class." That wasn't what she wanted to say, but she was sure Dani somehow knew that.

Dani winked. "I guess we should, too. I'll see you later?"

"Yep!"

"I got lucky and didn't see Noah for the rest of the day." Dani recounted her entire day for Claire as they walked to the car. They had a couple of classes together, but Dani would even talk about those. Or, more precisely, how she couldn't stop staring at Claire instead of doing actual work. It made Claire blush, which only spurred Dani on more.

"That's good. Weird, though, right? I mean, I have some classes with him, but he wasn't there."

"Eh, maybe he did something stupid and got kicked out again. I wouldn't be surprised."

"Maybe. Wanna drive?"

Dani grinned. "Yes! My place or yours?"

"Is your mom at work?" Dani nodded. "Yours, then. But I can't stay for long. I told Mom I'd be home tonight. Is that okay?"

"Yeah, of course!" Sure, Dani was disappointed. She wanted to spend every waking hour with Claire. But she wasn't stupid. She knew Claire had her family, her studies, her life. Dani wasn't about to be possessive and selfish.

"You know I'd rather be with you, right? It's just, mom

mentioned something about me spending a lot of time over at your place."

"Do you think she's suspicious?" Dani opened the car door for Claire, making sure she was all in before closing it. Then she ran around to the driver's side and hopped in. She started the car and instinctively turned down the volume on the radio. This was too important a conversation to be interrupted by blaring music.

"I don't know. I think maybe she's just worried about you, ya know? Ever since that day you came over after your mom hit you . . ."

"Slapped."

"Same thing, Dani."

"Not really but go on."

Claire rolled her eyes. "Fine, *slapped*. She's worried it'll get worse, and maybe I'll get caught up in it."

"I'd never let that happen."

Claire took Dani's hand. "I know." They continued to hold hands on the drive home. She may not be able to spend the night with Dani, but that didn't mean they couldn't utilize what time they did have.

"We're getting pretty good at this kissing stuff." Dani slipped her shirt over her head quickly, then got back to the kissing.

"We are," Claire agreed. "I don't have a lot of time, okay?"

"I know. So, hurry and catch up with me," Dani grinned.

Claire did precisely that. She had always been a bit more

modest than Dani. But when she was *with* Dani, all those insecurities and inhibitions seemed to disappear. Dani managed to make Claire feel beautiful, loved, wanted, and sexy all at the same time. It was quite heady for a teenager who wasn't used to *any* of those feelings.

Dani took a moment to appreciate the delicate lace bra Claire wore. She still couldn't believe how lucky she was to have seen what was underneath that bra. Underneath *everything*.

"Does your tummy do weird little flips when we're together?" she asked as she brought Claire close. They were still mostly dressed — sans shirts — but she couldn't wait to have her in her arms any longer. Besides, she thought it was more romantic if they undressed each other.

"Yes. And when I *think* about being with you or the things we've done already."

Dani smiled. "I love that feeling. Do you think it'll last forever?"

"I hope so." Claire lifted herself onto her toes and kissed Dani deeply. They really *were* getting good at this kissing stuff.

"What in the hell is going on here!"

Claire and Dani wrenched away from each other as though ice-cold water was thrown on them. Claire did her best to cover herself while blindly searching for the shirt she had just discarded. Dani merely stared — shirtless, mouth gaping open — at her mom.

Rita looked from Dani to Claire and back again. Her mind could barely process what she was seeing. She had received an anonymous call at work complaining about her daughter's immoral behavior. She had ignored similar calls earlier in the week, but a co-worker had caught wind of the multiple calls and made a rude comment. Embarrassed, Rita reluctantly took PTO and raced home. Whatever Dani was up to, it was going to stop. But she wasn't prepared for this.

"Mom, I —"

"Get out."

"What?"

"You have ten minutes to gather your shit and get out of my house."

"Mom!"

"Take your whore with you!"

"Don't talk about Claire like that!"

Rita's hand snaked out and slapped Dani hard across the face. "I will not have this in my house. Ten minutes." She turned and started for the door. Nausea threatened to bubble up. How could her daughter do this to her? Not only was she engaging in ungodly behavior, people *knew*! Rita was mortified. She stopped but didn't turn back. She couldn't bear to look at the scene again. "If your father were alive, this would surely kill him. Maybe he knew something was wrong with you, and that's what made him sick. Get out. I never want to see you in this house again."

That was it. The worst scenario just happened, and Dani's heart stopped. She swore it did. Her mother, the woman who was supposed to love her unconditionally, just kicked her out. If that blow didn't knock her out, blaming Dani for her father's death certainly did. Where the hell was she supposed to go?

"Dani?" Claire called out softly. She was scared, pissed, and heart-broken for her girlfriend. What kind of mother kicks her sixteen-year-old daughter out? "Come on, let's get some of your stuff. You can come home with me until your mom calms down. Then you can try talking to her."

"You heard her. She never wants to see me again." Dani's mind was racing as fast as her heart. Just minutes to go, she was blissfully happy. She could see a future. Now all she could see was the past. Her dad's kind eyes. Claire's cute smile. Dani would have to hold on to those to get through the present.

Dani's voice was eerily calm. Emotionless. But what Claire heard was a broken girl who had lost both parents now. "Maybe Mom could talk to her."

That brought Dani out of her daze. "No! Then they'll find out about you! About us!"

"I don't care, Dani." Claire was beginning to seriously panic. She knew Dani. She was as stubborn as a damn mule.

"I do! I won't have you kicked out, too!"

Claire wanted to argue that her mother would never do that. Would she? Of course, she didn't think Rita would have either.

"Dani, this is not the time to be stubborn." Claire hurriedly put on her shirt and looked around for her shoes. Meanwhile, Dani was rummaging around in her closet. "We can work this out."

Dani pulled out a duffle bag and began stuffing it with clothes. She didn't know if they were clean or dirty. It didn't matter. She was homeless now. Everything would be dirty soon. She thought about what Claire had said. Go home with her. Let Rita cool off a bit. Maybe try to talk some sense into her. But Dani knew Rita. She said what she meant and meant what she said. Wasn't it Dani's fear that something like this would happen all along? It was why she hid her true self from her mom.

But she couldn't burden Claire with this. No, she wouldn't risk Claire's relationship with her parents. The best thing Dani could do right now was disappear. Claire would be better off.

She could live happily in her home without worrying about her parents disowning her. She'd be off to college soon, and this little episode would be a distant memory. Besides, how could Claire love her if she became nothing more than a charity case? How could Claire love her if Dani's own mother couldn't love her? Dani would rather live in the streets than have Claire view her as a weak and needy nobody.

"Dani, are you listening to me?"

"No," Dani answered honestly. She had been too busy plotting where she'd go. She couldn't go to the pier. That would be the first place Claire looked.

Claire grabbed ahold of Dani's arm. "Will you stop for a minute and talk to me?"

"I only have ten minutes, Claire." Dani checked her watch. "More like five now."

"Just come home with me, okay? Everything will work out. I promise."

"How can you promise that? You don't know. You don't know if your parents would even let me stay. Think Rita's not going straight over there to tell them what's going on between us if she sees us headed that way? Get real, Claire."

Claire's eyes filled with tears. "So, what? Are you just going to live on the street? Don't be ridiculous. You have school. You have me."

"I have nothing," Dani said softly. "You don't need this shit in your life, Claire. You graduate in less than a month. Then you're off to college. What the fuck do you want some idiot like me in your life for?"

"Don't talk like that about yourself. Dani, please. I'll talk to my parents. I'll tell them everything. It may shock them at first, but they love you. *I* love you. Please, don't do this. You're making this decision based on emotions. How about we go get some ice cream, cool down, then we'll go talk to my parents."

Dani looked at her watch again as she stupidly crammed what toiletries she could in her bag. *Where am I going to use these at?* "Time's up. I gotta get out of here. Go home, Claire. Forget about me." *I'll love you forever. I'm sorry.*

That moment would be the one that haunted Dani every night. She would remember how her step stuttered when Claire begged her to stop. She would feel her heart break over and over when she heard Claire cry. And whatever bad things that would happen to her in the future, she would look back on this day — the day she let her pride triumph over her love for Claire — and know she deserved it.

CHAPTER SEVEN

What had she been thinking? She had no clue where she was going. No clue what she was doing. Why didn't she go home with Claire? Why did she have to let her freakin' ego get in her way? Now, Dani was walking aimlessly around town with a duffel bag and a broken heart. And she was terrified. She could turn around right now and walk to Claire's. She could call Claire and beg forgiveness and *hope* she would come to pick her up.

Dani took out her phone. Her finger was poised over Claire's name. It shook. Hell, her whole body was shaking. All those times she wished she could run away. How stupid could she have been? Life at home may not have been perfect, but she had a bed. She had food — most of the time. She had Claire. What did she have now? Her finger twitched, itching to press the send button and call Claire. It was that easy. And, yet, her stomach ached with dread. This wasn't Claire's burden. Dani couldn't risk ruining Claire's life. She was already afraid Rita blabbed everything to Claire's parents. She should call to make sure Claire was okay.

But she didn't call. Instead, she researched. *Where do homeless people go in Los Angeles?* Everything she read scared Dani more. She was sixteen. How was she going to take care of herself out on the streets? She didn't want to do drugs to get through the day. She absolutely didn't want to be a prostitute.

"Ugh! You made your damn decision, Dani. Time to grow up." She scrolled until she found the info she needed. *Skid Row.* Just the name made her skin crawl. Nevertheless, Dani turned off her phone to save battery, made sure she had her TAP card, and headed for the bus stop. Skid Row was about to become her home.

"Anything?" Claire stopped biting her nails long enough to ask the one-word question, then began again.

"No, Claire Bear. Are you sure this is the right place?"

"Yes! I remember because we missed the turn and had to go back. That was the pier she went to." Claire pointed towards Dani's secret hideout. She should have known that Dani wouldn't come here. Not after showing Claire where it was. But Claire had been hopeful.

After Dani walked away from her, Claire ran home and told her mom everything. At least she did the best should could between hiccupping sobs. She was filled with guilt and fear. Guilt because she should have run after Dani. She should have done whatever she possibly could to keep Dani from running away. But it was the fear that stopped her. What if Dani was right? What if Rita went to Claire's parents and the same thing happened? She had been selfish and weak, and now Dani was gone. It was when Claire lost sight of Dani that she decided to confess everything.

Karen had been confused. It took a herculean effort to decipher her daughter's ramblings, but once she did, Karen was stunned. Not that her daughter came out to her. Or that she and Dani were lovers. But that Rita could be so cruel as to say those things to Dani and kick her out. There were multiple times Karen wanted to knock some sense into Rita. Right now, all she wanted to do was knock Rita out. No *real* mother kicked their child out for being gay. What the hell year was it in Rita's fucked up mind? Instead of going to give Rita a piece of her mind, Karen and Jose jumped into the car with Claire and began their search for Dani.

"Stay here," Jose grumbled. "I'm going to go talk to the groundskeeper."

He tried keeping his cool for his daughter's sake. Inside he was fuming. He *knew* he should have confronted Rita about her behavior. Perhaps if he had, Dani wouldn't be missing right now. Jose refused to say Dani ran away. She may have made the choice — the wrong choice — but she was pushed into it by an uncaring piece of shit of a mother. When he asked Claire why Dani didn't come home with her, Claire just sobbed harder. It broke his heart, and he was determined to do what he could to mend *Claire's* broken heart.

"Did he see her?" Claire asked as soon as her dad got back in the car.

"No. I gave him our number and asked him to give us a call if he did."

"What do we do now?" Claire asked.

"Can we go to the police?" Karen asked Jose. Law was his area of expertise, having been a lawyer for more than fifteen years.

"I think we might have to. We're not her family . . ."

"Yes, we are!" Claire interjected heatedly.

"Claire Bear, I'm talking legally here. Of course, we are her family, and we'll take her in as soon as we find her. We can report her as a runaway, report Rita for neglect, and continue to look."

"Will Rita get in trouble for what she did?" Claire wanted Rita to pay. She didn't deserve to live happy and free after what she did.

"She could," Jose confirmed. "Child neglect is only a misdemeanor, though. The harshest punishment Rita could see is a year in jail and a fine."

"That's not enough!" Claire cried. "Dani is out on the *streets*! Alone! What if she gets hurt? Or killed?"

Karen turned in her seat and took her daughter's hand. "Let's not think that way, Claire Bear."

"We have to, Mom!"

"*If* Dani is hurt while out on the streets because her mother kicked her out," Jose interrupted, "Rita could be charged with a felony. That could include six years in state prison and a fine. But, Claire Bear, it could also mean probation. The law is not as black and white as people would like to think. Now, we're going to continue our search, and I'll call a contact I have at the LAPD."

"Wait, will Dani get in trouble for running away?"

"I don't think so, sweetheart. She was forced out. So, unless she's caught in a crime, she'll be returned to us. I'm going to spell out the situation and see about becoming Dani's guardian." He looked at Claire in the rearview mirror. "I'm going to fight for the strongest punishment I can get for Rita, Claire Bear. For Dani *and* you."

She wanted to cry but knew she couldn't. She wanted to run back home but knew she couldn't. She wanted to call Claire but knew she shouldn't. That was the extent of what Dani knew. What she *didn't* know was where she was going to sleep, eat, or even go to the bathroom. She had precisely $8.32 in her pocket and no clue how to make that last. Suddenly, crackers, questionable meat, and sprouting potatoes seemed like a feast. She didn't even know what kind of clothes she stuffed in her duffle. Did she bring a jacket? Socks? Underwear?

"What do we have here?"

Dani froze. She didn't dare turn around to see if they were talking about her. She was too afraid they were. The voice was saccharine sweet in that "I'm going to kill you with a smile" way. The kind of voice that chilled you to the bone because you just knew it belonged to someone who wouldn't think twice before hurting you. She tried not to whimper when someone bumped into her.

"Don't be shy, little girl. Tell us your name."

Dani stole an intimidated glance at the men who surrounded her. Boys really. They couldn't have been much older than she was. But they were hardened. Tattoos littered their bodies in no particular order that she could see. Perhaps they told the story of their time out here on the streets. Then, Dani wondered how they could afford tattoos if they lived out here on the streets. Her sixteen-year-old mind wasn't comprehending anything at the moment.

One of the guys pushed her shoulder hard. "You heard him! What's your fucking name?"

"D-Dani."

"Dani?" The one who seemed to be the leader laughed. "You wanna be a boy?"

Dani nearly scoffed. She *hated* that question. "No."

"Why you dress like one?" The guy flicked her hard on the arm. When she didn't answer right away, he bunched her t-shirt up in his hand and pulled her to him. "You're gonna wanna work on answering me when I ask you questions."

His breath stunk, and she still couldn't bring herself to look him in the eye. Somewhere deep down, she didn't want to know what he looked like. She didn't want to see the color of his skin, the color of his eyes, the color of his hair, or whether he had hair. She didn't want to see any of that in her nightmares.

"I j-just like the clothes," she answered timidly. "They're comfortable."

He snorted. "Yeah, I suppose they are. Better than that frilly shit most girls wear. Though that shit is fucking hot, right guys?"

"Fuck yeah!" his crew answered enthusiastically.

The leader released his grip on Dani and smoothed out the wrinkles he created. "Since you're not my type, we're going to have to work something else out."

Dani's stomach dropped. She wasn't even out here for an hour, and already she was in trouble. Did it freakin' follow her? "W-what?" She tried grabbing at her duffel when someone took it from her. "That's mine!"

The leader's hand was swiftly around Dani's throat. "Ain't nothin' yours out here. It's all mine."

"But it's all I have," Dani cried.

"Not anymore. It's payment for me allowing you to stay here in Skid Row." He looked over at his goons.

The smallest of the group was going through the duffel bag. "Clothes and a charger for a phone," he announced.

"A charger? That must mean you have a phone on you."

Please, no.

"What did I say about answering, bitch?"

"Y-yes."

He laughed. "She stupid or something?" he asked his friends, causing them to laugh, too. "Get your phone out and give it to me."

Since his hand was still around her throat, she didn't hesitate to do as she was told. It pained her greatly to know that her lifeline to Claire was now going into this dude's pocket.

"Good girl. Now," he let her go, finally. "Let's discuss next week's payment."

"I — I don't have anything left. You took it all." She *wasn't* stupid enough to tell him about the $8.32 that was in one of her other pockets.

"You got options," he said. "Start panhandlin'. Whatever you make, I get sixty percent. But that only works if you're makin' some bank. I require at least a hundred bucks to let you stay here."

A hundred bucks? I'd be able to get a freakin' apartment for that! She sure as shit didn't say that out loud. And even though she was certain she didn't want to know the answer, she asked the question that was hanging over her head. "What happens if I can't come up with that?"

She barely got out the last word before all the breath left her body. With one blow to her stomach, he had stolen not only her breath, but her ability to stand, and very nearly her will to live.

One freakin' hour. That's how long she was going to survive on the freakin' street.

"Does that answer your question?" he asked with a smirk.

Dani nodded painfully.

"Now, if panhandlin' ain't for you, you'll become my mule."

Flashes of drug-filled balloons or condoms being shoved up or down various holes went through Dani's head. She'd seen enough movies and played enough games with gangsters to know this wouldn't end well for her at all.

"A hundred bucks minimum this time next week, got me? Otherwise, you and me? We gonna have issues."

Though Dani had no clue how she was going to come up with anywhere *close* to a hundred bucks, she nodded. Hell, she would agree to almost anything if it meant he would leave her alone for at least a week. She waited until their laughter faded before she even dared to move. Once she thought it was safe, Dani struggled to stand up straight. She had been hit twice now, and she had to admit, she didn't like it at all.

Go home to Claire! her mind yelled at her. But her freakin' ego wouldn't allow it. Even after everything that just happened, her stupid ass couldn't let go of her pride. Or perhaps now it was even worse. It had been one freakin' hour. If she couldn't make it on her own, what the hell good was she to Claire? Dani ignored the logical side of her that told her she was only sixteen and shouldn't have to worry about making it on her own yet. She blocked out the voice that told her grown adults who were here on Skid Row weren't "making it on their own." Right now, she had more important things to worry about, like where to freakin' sit down before she passed out.

Dani walked, taking everything in with a child's eye. Did

people know this place existed? That there were thousands of human beings literally living on the streets? How could this be possible? Did everyone's family turn them away? The area was littered with stuff. If there wasn't a tent, box, or tarp, in your way, there was litter of all kinds. Some things Dani didn't want to think about, let alone step in. She avoided eye contact with people yelling in the wind or sitting in their wheelchairs, asking for money, or throwing things at passersby.

There was one man in particular that caught Dani's attention, though she tried hard not to stare. He was old. Had to be in his seventies at least. He sat quietly in a tiny corner under a makeshift shelter made from frayed cardboard boxes. He didn't say a word, didn't make a sound. Just watched Dani walk by and gave her a slight nod. It was the first person she had made eye contact with in this Godforsaken place, and it broke her heart even more than it already was. How long had he been out here? How had he survived? How, since he had no legs?

She kept walking — because she could — looking for any minuscule place that maybe she could call her own. She studied some of the "housing" around her and realized she'd have to find her own box soon. It'd be good to be out of the elements, even if just a little. Now, if she had a tent, that would be even better. Some of the tents around her had holes, but they still looked cozier than sleeping on the concrete out in the open. She wondered if any of the shelters she read about could give her one. Did they do that? Thinking of shelters got Dani thinking about food. She had read something on the bus ride here that there was a soup kitchen or whatever it was called somewhere around here. She dug into her pocket to get her phone out when she remembered how and why she didn't have it anymore.

Dani ducked into a fenced area, catching her shirt on the jagged edge of the hole that was cut as a doorway. There wasn't one spot that wasn't covered with someone's meager belongings. She sighed with defeat. Dani's stomach was still hurting from being punched, though she was pretty sure she was also feeling the beginnings of hunger pangs. It was probably all in her head. She was afraid she wouldn't be able to find food out here, so, of course, now she *really* needed food. Before, she was able to forget about eating altogether when she was deeply invested in a video game.

"Watch it!"

Dani snapped out of her stupor, nearly tripping over some dude's — kitchen? Okay, so it was, like, a burner that people used for camping, but Dani was pretty sure it would still burn if she fell on it.

"Sorry! I'm sorry!" She walked away briskly, bumping into other people and other people's things. Had she always been this freakin' clumsy? Or was this place way overcrowded? As she stumbled around, Dani finally saw the first bit of real estate that looked unoccupied. It was barely big enough to fit her ass if she sat down, but it would have to do. She hurried over to the spot.

"I wouldn't sit there if I was you."

Dani looked around to where the voice came from. The dude was caked with dirt, but then everyone around here was. His hair was long and scraggly. His beard looked as though a family of vermin lived in there. She looked back at the bare spot, then at him again.

"Why?"

"Ain't your spot."

"It doesn't look like anyone's spot," Dani said

apprehensively. She was afraid she was going to get hit again if she mouthed off too much. But she was tired. All she wanted to do was sit down.

"Every spot is someone's spot." The bearded dude shuffled over to her.

Dani crossed her arms over her stomach and wondered if she should get in some kind of boxing stance. She didn't know how to box, but everyone knew to hold your hands up to protect the face.

"Spots is hard t'git," bearded dude continued. "Don't know whatya did, but you can't sit there."

"I just got here. I didn't do anything." *Except lose all my stuff in less time than it took to pack it.*

"Musta done sumpin'. C'mon."

He gestured for Dani to follow him, and like an idiot, she did.

"Where are we going? I don't have any money. I don't have anything."

"None us do, Kid. 'Cept Angel says you're to be taken care of."

Dani stopped in her tracks and watched bearded dude drag one leg as he walked. "What do you mean 'taken care of'?"

He looked back at her and cackled. "You look scared, Kid."

"My name is . . ."

"Nah! No names. They call me Beard. Carts lives here," he pointed at a run-down tent to their left. "Pick lives there. You're Kid." He shrugged. "You get useta it if you stick around. But if ya are stickin' 'round, Angel says you gotta stay here."

Dani took in the sweet, big tent he was standing in front of.

It was red and at least double the size of the others surrounding it.

"What?"

The question sounded as dumb as she felt. But, honestly, she had no clue what the hell was going on. She went from having a home and a girlfriend to having a duffel bag, to having nothing. Now she had a tent? And who the hell was this Angel person? What did they want from Dani in return?

"This here's yours now." Beard unzipped the flap of the tent, and she gestured for her to go in.

Nope. Not going in there with some strange guy. "Um."

Beard stepped back and held his hands up. "Not gonna hurt ya, Kid. First all, Angel will kill me. Second, we gotta watch out for ya. Stuff's in there. You want it, go for it. Ain't no skin off my back if ya don't." He scratched at his beard. "Yeah, it is. C'mon, Kid. Just take a look to see I ain't messin' with ya."

Dani bent slightly and peered into the tent. There was a semi-clean sleeping bag, a pillow, a burner like the one she nearly toppled over before, and — she did a double-take — her duffle bag.

"What's going on here? Why is my duffle bag here? What does this Angel want from me in return for all this?" Dani forgot about being scared for a minute. Right now, she was pissed, tired, hungry, and confused. When she got like this, Claire always said Dani got mouthy. Her attitude was either going to get her answers or get her killed. At this point, she wasn't sure which one she would welcome more.

"Angel got it back for ya. Got hit by the Landlords, yeah? They told ya you owe them rent? Took your stuff as the first payment?"

"Yeah."

Beard nodded. "They hit everyone. 'Cept, now we have Angel. Angel don't do this for everyone but says you're young. Says ya need a chance if ya gonna survive."

"What do I have to do?" Dani wasn't that experienced, but she knew nothing in life was free. That had to be especially true out here on the streets.

Beard shook his head. "Just gotta do some good. See these?" He lifted his foot to show her his shoes. Despite the looks of the rest of him, the shoes were in spectacular condition. They were the type of shoes that would allow you to walk miles before your feet would even think about hurting. "Landlords stole my shoes and roughed me up for not being able to pay rent. Next thing I know, I got these babies. Kid, the only thing Angel asks in return is that ya help with helping, ya know? Me? I got ya. I'm supposed to show you around, get you some food and stuff. That ain't a high price to pay for these. So, c'mon. Let me do my job."

"Hey, Sister!" Beard shouted across the room. He received a big smile in return from an older black woman wearing a habit that Dani had only ever seen in movies.

"Beard, what did I tell you about shouting?" Sister scolded playfully when they finally got to her.

Beard actually blushed — at least Dani thought he did under all that dirt — and grinned.

"Sorry, Sister. But I brought you 'nother mouth!"

Sister looked at Dani and frowned. "How old are you, child?"

"It's Kid," Beard answered quickly. "And she's eighteen. Right, Kid?"

"Uh." Dani looked at Beard and then at Sister. Was she going to go to hell for lying to a nun? "Yes."

"Do you have an ID?" Sister asked suspiciously.

"Landlords got to her," Beard answered again. "Took everything."

"Are you going to let the girl answer, Beard? Or do I have to separate you two to get my answers."

"Nah, you don't have to separate us. I was just tryin' ta help like Angel asked."

"Angel is looking out for her?"

Dani couldn't tell if Sister was intrigued or more suspicious.

"Yeah?" Beard shrugged.

"Young lady, can you tell me why you're out here? Beard, if you say a word, I am going to tell them to forget your cornbread."

Beard effectively closed his mouth.

"Same as anyone else, I suppose," Dani answered carefully. "Down on my luck and all that."

Sister raised a brow. "Family?" Dani shook her head. "There's no one you can stay with?"

"No. I'm on my own. And I'm really hungry. Do I have to pay for this food? Cuz I don't have any money."

"No, child, this food is free. But I would like to speak to you about going to a women's shelter. Someone like you shouldn't be out here by yourself."

"Uh, Sister?" Beard spoke up timidly. "Not tryna step on

your toes, but that's the first place the Landlords will look for Kid. She's under Angel's wing now, but ya know they don't give up that easy. If they see Kid isn't protected, they comin' after her."

Dani's stomach dropped. How could she be stupid enough to think all that shit with the "Landlords" would be over now that she got her stuff back.

Sister sighed. As much as she hated to admit Beard was right, she couldn't deny he was. Angel was both a blessing and sometimes a curse around Skid Row. Sister knew Angel was trying to do good where good was scarce. Unfortunately, that caused the bad to be worse when Angel wasn't around.

"Fine. But if you need *anything*, you come and see me. I also want to get you set up with SNAP."

Dani's brows furrowed. "SNAP?"

"Food stamps," Sister explained.

"Just somethin' else for Landlords to take," Beard scoffed. "Plus, ya gotta be active about lookin' for a job."

"Beard."

"Sorry, Sister." Effectively chastised, Beard took his tray of food from the volunteer. "I'll go save us a seat, Kid."

"He's not wrong," Sister admitted. "The government will provide you with a card and fill it each month with an amount you qualify for. Unless you are disabled — mentally or physically — pregnant, or *under eighteen*," she gave Dani a look. "You have to have a job or visit a work program. I'll go over all that if it's something you might be interested in."

"Okay." Dani felt like crying. Her head was spinning. The Landlords, Angel, Beard, Sister, and all the different things she needed to do, fill out, or learn — Dani was in over her head. For the millionth time since she walked away from Claire, Dani wanted to call her. But she couldn't. "Uh, Sister?"

"Yes?"

"I do have one question." Dani shuffled her feet and cleared her throat. "Where, uh, where do I go to the bathroom out here on the streets? And, uh, get, you know, products?"

Sister gave her a small smile. It broke her heart to see someone so young out on the streets. But she made a promise years ago when she started volunteering to help the homeless never to force anyone to talk to her. She believed when it was time for them, they would come to her. And she would do everything she could to help them. Sister Haywood believed Dani would come to her one day with why she was *truly* out here on her own. Until then, she could steer her in the right direction.

"Come with me," Sister smiled. "Don't worry. There will still be food for you. And if Angel tasked Beard with looking out for you, he'll be here when we get back, too."

Chapter Eight

"Where's your *girlfriend?* I heard she was put in a looney bin."
Noah snickered and fist-bumped his friends.

"Go away, Noah."

It had been two weeks since Dani disappeared, and Claire
was as miserable as ever. She and her parents continued to go out
every night to look for Dani to no avail. Her dad said the
authorities were "looking into" Dani's situation, but so far, they'd
done nothing. Rita hadn't even been punished yet. Apparently,
they were still investigating that as well. Claire didn't
understand what needed to be investigated. The hateful woman
threw her only child out on the streets simply because she was
gay. That's *at least* the definition of child neglect. But Rita told
the authorities that Dani ran away and Claire's — being the
girlfriend — side of the story wasn't being taken as serious.

"Aww, poor thing. You don't have much of a bite when your
dog isn't around, huh?"

Claire clenched her hands into fists. She seriously
considered throwing her tray of uneaten food at him. Then she
thought about Dani out there on the streets. Was she eating?
Was she safe? Claire had been reading too much about
homelessness in Los Angeles. It was scary to think Dani was out
there all by herself. She learned of Skid Row and begged her dad
to go looking for Dani there. He did—every night. And every
night he returned alone, Claire's hope faded more and more.

"Leave her alone!"

Noah laughed. "Are you serious? You have a little freshman doing your fighting for you now?"

Claire gave Lulu a small smile. "It's okay."

"No, it's not. We're tired of him being a bully!"

Suddenly, others who had been bullied for who they are surrounded them. They looked as scared as mice in a snake pit, but they stood their ground.

"You know you're only making things worse for yourselves, right?" Noah sneered. "Go play. The grown-ups are talking. Well, one at least."

"You are so far from being a grown-up, Noah," Claire said. "You're a scared, lonely little boy. You're so incredibly miserable that you have to make others miserable to make yourself feel better. Your parents couldn't care less about you. They go on vacations without you, don't come to your basketball games, and probably wouldn't notice if you never graduated. I get it. You're not loved at home, and that sucks. But that doesn't give you the right to be an asshole to everyone, Noah."

"You little b . . ."

"Mr. Anderson, I urge you not to be late for your next class. You already have detention for two weeks." Principal Stevens crossed his arms and watched Noah grumble as he walked away. "Miss Oliver, can I see you in my office, please?"

"I didn't say anything wrong, Mr. Stevens," Claire said as she walked in the principal's office. Dani had been here many times. Claire, however, had not, and she was nervous as heck! Yet, if she was honest with herself, she didn't care if he suspended her at this point. It would just give her more time to look for Dani.

"While I can't officially agree with how you handled things, this isn't about your conversation with Mr. Anderson, Claire. Have a seat."

"I only spoke the truth," she mumbled as she sat obediently.

"Be that as it may, I'm supposed to tell you that airing other people's problems in public is not the right thing to do. But I'll say again, that is not why you're here."

"Then why?"

"Miss Reed has not been in school for the past two weeks. I've tried calling her home only to be told she doesn't live there any longer. You and she were close, and I was hoping to get some information. Have you heard from her?"

Tears welled up in Claire's eyes. "No, sir. Not since her mother kicked her out."

Principal Stevens's eyes widened. "Kicked her out?"

Claire nodded, a lump forming in her throat. It was hard for her to talk about Dani, but maybe if she could get her principal to believe her, he could help with the authorities. With that in mind, she told him the whole story. Including the part where she and Dani were girlfriends. It was the first time she had officially "come out" to anyone other than her family. It was . . . freeing.

Principal Stevens sat back in his chair and blew out a breath. "I had no idea. Well, I knew Dani was, um . . ."

"Gay? A lesbian? Homosexual?" Claire offered cheekily.

Principal Stevens gave her a small smile. "Yes. I don't understand how her mother didn't already know."

"Dani always said that her mom only saw what she wanted to see. Whatever made her look better in people's eyes. When she saw the truth, she couldn't handle it. And now Dani is out there on the streets."

"Surely, there was another option than putting her child in danger."

"I tried to get Dani to come home with me. But she was afraid my parents would do the same to me. Not to mention that da . . . dang ego of hers."

"What do the authorities say?" He took a moment to remind himself this was probably not an appropriate conversation to be having with a student. Unfortunately, he hadn't been getting any answers from Mrs. Reed.

"They're not taking it seriously. They say she's a runaway, so what do they care what happens to her?"

Principal Stevens realized that was most likely Claire's opinion more than an accurate depiction of what was going on.

"We've been looking for her every day," Claire continued. "My dad goes out for hours, driving around looking for her. I'm afraid something has happened to her."

"I'm going to call your parents and see what I can do to help," Principal Stevens stated with authority. "I know people who work at some of the shelters downtown. I'll make some calls and see if anyone has seen Dani."

"Thank you, Mr. Stevens. I'll tell my parents to expect your call."

Claire ran into the dining room, skidding to a stop, and scaring her parents. "Skid Row!"

Jose looked at Karen with concern. "What about it, Claire Bear?"

"That's where she has to be!" Claire put her iPad on the table and pointed at the screen. "It's where the homeless go. We could go there and ask around. Surely someone has seen her."

"Honey, I drive by there every night. I haven't seen her."

"Drive-by," Claire rolled her eyes. "You can't just drive by, Dad. You have to get out and ask around. I'll go with you."

"Claire Bear, that's a dangerous place to be."

"They're homeless, Dad — not murderers. Plus, if Dani is there, we need to bring her home. I don't think she would leave with you."

"I'm sorry, but the answer is no. That's final."

Claire frowned at her father. "Do you even care if we find her? Did you really go to the police about Rita?"

"Claire, I know you're upset, but do not speak to your father like that," Karen scolded. She gave her daughter the "mom look" when Claire opened her mouth to argue. "He has been out there looking for Dani every night since she disappeared. *Every* night."

Claire sat down in the chair closest to her father and tried not to let the tears fall. "I know. I'm sorry, Dad. I don't know what else to do. I've thought about camping out by her pier or putting cameras up. I'm worried about her. I'm so afraid something has happened to her, and reading about Skid Row didn't help."

"I understand, Claire Bear." Jose took Claire's hand. "We're all worried about Dani. I'll have Lieutenant Chi come with me to Skid Row, and we'll do a more thorough search. I'm secure enough in my masculinity to admit that place scares me."

Claire offered him a small smile. She knew he was trying to make a joke for her sake, but if *he* was scared, Dani had to be terrified. Thinking about Dani being out there all alone hurt Claire's heart. She had read about people being beaten for no reason or turning to drugs. Or prostitution. Bile began to rise in her throat, and she sprang up from the chair.

"I, um, have some homework."

"Claire!"

"Let her go, Jose."

"I'm an idiot. I shouldn't have said that." Jose buried his head in his hands.

"Probably not," Karen agreed. "She most likely understood what you were trying to do. Unfortunately, she's now thinking about Dani being out there in a place a big, strong man like you is afraid of."

Jose peeked up at his wife. "Thanks."

She shrugged. "Sorry. But now I'm thinking about it, too." Karen sat down and sighed. "Why didn't she come home with Claire? We've treated her like a daughter for ten years. She should have known we'd welcome her with open arms."

"Karen, the kid just had her heart ripped out, stomped on, and thrown back in her face by her *mother*. How much trust would you have in *anyone* after that? Plus, she was caught in a compromising situation with our daughter. After her mother's reaction, she was probably scared we'd kill her or kick Claire out with her."

"We wouldn't have had the same reaction as that bitch Rita!" Karen said heatedly. "How anyone can even call that woman a mother is beyond me. She's a vessel. A walking fallopian tube. An incubator. Nothing more. But, oh, a *whole* lot less."

Jose grinned at his wife's fiery retort. "Why don't you tell me how you really feel?"

"It's not funny," she said with less conviction. "That poor child is out there suffering. And *our* child is suffering in return."

"I know, honey. Why do you think I'm going out every night looking for her?" He glanced toward the door. "I don't understand the lifestyle, Karen, but I love my daughter with all my heart. When her heart breaks, so does mine. I need to find Dani. I need them *both* to know that I'm on their side. One-hundred percent."

Karen leaned over and kissed him on the cheek. "This is why I married you." She sighed again. "I'm going to make Claire a sandwich. She hasn't been eating. She hasn't been sleeping. She graduates soon, but she doesn't want to think about that now. College was something she'd been looking forward to, but now. . ."

"Now all she can think about is Dani," Jose finished for her. He brought out his phone and sent a quick text. The phone chimed immediately with an answer. "I'm going out to Skid Row with Chi."

"I'll make two more sandwiches."

"Claire?" Karen rapped on the door before pushing it open.

She caught her daughter with one leg out the window. "Claire! Where on earth do you think you're going!"

"I can't just sit around here while Dani is out there!"

"Were you planning on going to Skid Row by yourself?" Claire shrugged. "Young lady, I know you've read what happens there."

"Exactly! I have! Which means if Dani is there, I need to go get her!"

"Claire . . ."

"I'm going, Mom. If Dad —"

"Your dad left fifteen minutes ago with Lieutenant Chi. Like every other night, he's going out to look for Dani." She held her arms open for a sobbing Claire. "Trust your father to do everything he can to find her."

"I love her, Mom. So much. What am I going to do if something . . .?"

"We're not going to go there, sweetheart. But we have to come to terms with the fact that maybe Dani doesn't want to be found." Karen nudged Claire to sit on the bed and knelt in front of her. "I know that girl loves you. I've seen it in her eyes. But what happened to her. What Dani's own mother did to her has to be weighing so heavily on her heart that she can't see past it."

"You mean, like, if her mother can't love her, how can I?"

Karen nodded sadly. Five minutes with Rita would help her anger. But it wouldn't help either Claire or Dani.

"Wait, you *knew* about Dani and me?"

"No, I knew Dani loved you. I think when you're a parent, you tend to have blinders on when it comes to your own kids."

"You don't like that I'm gay."

"I didn't say that, Claire Bear. But it's not something I would have chosen for you."

"I didn't *choose* this."

Karen sighed again. "I'm not explaining this right. Dani could have been a boy, and I still would've had blinders on when it came to you. You're still my sweet, little girl. I never want to think about you growing up, having *feelings*, or, ahem, having sex. Yet, here you are. Doing all three of those things."

"Mom!"

Karen chuckled. "What? We probably should've had this discussion a long time ago. At least Dani can't get you pregnant."

"Mom!" Claire flopped back onto her bed and threw her arm over her eyes. She felt the bed dip beside her. Yeah, it was embarrassing talking to your mom about sex. But she was glad *her* mom still loved and supported her. "Thank you," she whispered.

"For what?"

"Loving me."

A tear rolled down Karen's temple as she lay beside her daughter. Her answer should have been as simple as "that's what mothers do."

"Always."

CHAPTER NINE

It's been almost a year since I've seen you, Claire. I miss you every day. Not a day goes by that I don't kick myself for making the biggest mistake of my life. But every time I tried to call you to fix things, I got scared. Days turned into weeks. Weeks into months. You've probably forgotten all about me by now. I wouldn't blame you. I'm nothing to remember. I wasn't when I was there. I'm even less so now. I don't think you'd even recognize me.

You graduated. I wish I could have been there to see you get your diploma. I'm afraid if I see you, it will break me, and I have to be strong out here. So don't tell anyone that I cry myself to sleep every night. OK? You'll be starting college soon. I hope you find someone worthy of you, which is kinda impossible. I wish I could have been worthy of you. I wish I had come home with you. I wish I could have been strong enough to . . . I wish a lot of things, Claire.

It's been rough out here, but I think I have it easier than a lot of people around me. There's food. Sister — she's a nun at the shelter — has helped me a lot. I won't tell you what it's like to be a teenaged girl out on the streets without easy access to a clean bathroom. I live in a tent. It's not mine, but for some reason, someone's looking out for me. I pretend that I'm camping. Do you remember that time we went camping? You hated it. It was hot. The bugs were like pterodactyls, the fish never bit. But, for me, it will always be special. We slept in the same tent, remember? There was one point at night when you rolled over and put your

*arm around me. I knew you were dead to the world and didn't
know what you were doing, but I still think about that. I
pretended that you loved me, and we were together. I think we
were, like, twelve and thirteen or something. God I loved you.*

*I still do. I guess I always will. I have written you, like, a ton
of letters all saying everything I couldn't say before. I don't know
why I do it since I know you'll never read them. Or maybe that is
why. I don't know. It helps me, though, ya know? Sister says I can
talk to her if I need to. And Beard is here. Oh man, he's cray-cray
but pretty cool. I think you'd like him. But I don't want to talk to
them about you. You're too, I don't know, sacred or something.
Did I spell that right? Oh well, who cares?*

*I think I told you in one of my other letters that we don't use
names out here. Sometimes I feel like I'm losing my identity. I
used to use pictures of you to help me remember. Or listen to an
old voicemail you sent me just to hear your voice and ground me.
But my phone has been dead for a while now. I lost my charger,
and I only had eight bucks to my name. I thought I should
probably save that for food or something cuz I can't get food
stamps. I'm not old enough. One more year and I'll be eighteen.
I'll be able to get them then.*

*I guess I'll go for now. It's getting late and they stop serving
food soon. But I needed to get this letter written today. I love you,
Claire. Happy birthday.*

"What's this?"

The paper Dani was writing on was snatched out from
under her hand. She looked up and saw a girl — maybe a couple
of years older than her — reading her letter. The girl was the
total opposite of Claire. Tall, curvy, darker-skinned, long black
hair. This girl should *not* be the one reading the letter.

"Give that back."

The girl giggled wickedly. "I'm not done yet. Ooo, I love love letters!"

"Give it back!" Dani grabbed at the paper, but the girl was taller and held it up high. "Son of a bitch! That's not yours!"

"Everything in Skid Row is mine. Yous been riding for free up 'til now, *kid*."

Dani growled when the girl danced around her, waving the letter around. She was taunting Dani like those damn kids at school used to do. After nearly a year on the streets, Dani wasn't a newbie anymore. Angel and Beard did a good job of keeping her safe — even though she still hadn't come face to face with the elusive savior. But they couldn't be everywhere at every moment, and Dani had gotten in a few scuffles with people who thought they could take advantage of the "kid." She was sick of it. She dug a knife out of her pocket and flipped it open.

"Give it back to me, now," she said between clenched teeth.

The people around them scattered at the sight of the knife — everyone except Sister and Beard.

"You don' wanna do this, Kid," Beard said cautiously. "Angel wouldn't approve."

"Yeah, well, *I* don't approve of being made fun of anymore!" Dani shouted. "All I want is my letter back and for this chick to leave me the eff alone!"

"Viper, give the letter back, please." Sister tried to keep her voice as calm as possible. Viper was volatile. And Kid seemed to have hit her limit with Skid Row. Unfortunately, since Kid refused classes or disclosing her actual age, Sister was afraid Skid Row would be "home" for a long time.

"I was just messin' around." Viper tossed the piece of paper on the floor. "Not my fault she can't take a joke."

"*Bitch*," Dani muttered.

She caught the murderous look Viper gave her right before it turned into a sneer.

"See you around, kid." Viper got as close as she could without putting herself within stabbing distance. "You ain't gone be protected 24/7. And my knife is bigger than yours."

Dani took a half-hearted swipe at her.

"Kid! Put the dang knife down! If Angel caught you . . ."

"Angel, Angel, Angel!" Dani screeched. "Where is this Angel? Does he/she even exist? I've never met them!"

"Who ya think got yer stuff back for ya? Don't be ungrateful, Kid." Beard braved Dani's temper tantrum and held his hand out for the knife.

"No. I need this! That Viper person was right. I'm not going to be protected by you or Angel or even Sister 24/7. I need to learn to protect myself!"

"Fine. I ain't gonna take yer knife. But," he looked back at Sister, who nodded. "You can't bring it in here anymore. It's too dangerous fer e'eryone else. There are families here. Kids. Ya wanna keep that tent of yers, you gotta agree to that."

Dani thought about where she would go if she lost the tent. She remembered her first day on Skid Row and how crowded it was. In the weeks and months that have passed, it had only become more crowded. There were days when she got to the shelter late, and most of the food was gone. Sister was good enough to Dani to save items for her that Sister knew Dani needed. Yeah, she tried — consistently — to get Dani to go to classes and do work assignments, but that was her job. It wasn't like she actually cared what happened to her. At least that's what Dani kept telling herself. It was easier to believe.

"I won't bring it here anymore," Dani agreed. "But maybe you could tell Angel to get these people to leave me alone! I'm so sick of it! Every effing day of my life, *someone* felt the need to bully me. I ain't going to take it anymore!" She almost didn't even feel bad for saying ain't. But she could see the scowl on Claire's face. "I'm outta here."

Dani stuffed her knife into her pocket and stormed out. She wondered if she asked nicely if Beard would introduce her to Angel. And maybe Angel would show her how to protect herself. What if she never got off the streets? One day, someone was going to get to her when she was the most vulnerable. That's just how the world worked.

"I don't ask for much."

The raspy voice caught Dani off guard. She dug clumsily in her pocket and realized if she had been in real danger, she'd probably be dead by now.

"I give you shelter. Protection. I only ask that you stay out of trouble."

"Angel?" Dani squinted in the direction the voice came from. She was completely confused. Intrigued, but confused. She couldn't see anyone, but the pitch of the voice was unmistakable. "You're a woman."

"That surprises you? You think only a man can be a protector?"

"Well, no. I don't know. People fear you. I guess I just, like, assumed you were some gigantic, seven-foot-tall dude." She heard a chuckle come from the shadows and took a curious step forward.

"Strength comes from within, Kid. It's knowledge. Experience. Brute physicality can only get you so far if your opponent can outsmart you."

Dani turned quickly as the voice now came from behind her. "How?"

"You live in the shadows long enough, Kid, and you become the shadow."

"Show me how," Dani begged the darkness.

"You shouldn't be here."

"But I am here!"

"Why?"

"Does it matter? This is my home now. Teach me how to protect myself. Please?"

"Why, Kid?"

Dani sighed. She didn't think she'd get away with not answering Angel's questions. But she had questions of her own. "Okay. If I answer that, will you answer one of mine?"

"We'll see. Why are you here?"

"My mom kicked me out."

"For?"

"Um." Dani shuffled her feet. What if Angel didn't like gay people either? Dani was suddenly afraid of the shadows.

"You have nothing to fear from me, Kid. Was it drugs? Did you steal from her?"

Dani scoffed. "No. I fell in love with my best friend. My mom caught us kissing and stuff. Turns out, she doesn't want some homo living in her house."

Angel stepped out of the shadows. It didn't help much as she was clad in dark clothes and a hoodie that covered her face. "You're out here because you're a lesbian?"

Dani blushed. She was all bravado when she was defending who she was to bullies. She was able to say the word when she was with Claire. But she had never said the word out loud to a stranger.

"Yeah, I guess."

"You guess you're a lesbian?"

"No. I mean, yes. I mean, I *am*! I guess I'm here because my so-called mother couldn't deal."

"And your girlfriend? Did she abandon you, too?"

"No! Claire would *never* do that!"

"Yet, she isn't here, nor are you with her."

"You don't know anything!"

Angel stayed calm in the face of Dani's frustration. "Enlighten me."

The anger left Dani like air out of a popped balloon. "She wanted to help me," she confessed. "She begged me to go home with her."

"But?"

"I couldn't risk her parents kicking her out, too. They didn't know she was, um, with me."

Angel knew there was more to the story. More to the Kid's reason for disappearing instead of accepting help. She knew because she was the same way. Her pride always seemed to get in the way. Angel saw a lot of herself in this young kid. And that's what scared her the most.

"You should get in touch with her. Let her help."

Dani shook her head. "It's too late. She hates me by now. Can I ask you a question now?" Angel shrugged. "I guess I understand why they call you Angel. But why do you hide?"

"I'm no angel. I do what I do to try and keep the peace

around here. People are already down on their luck. They don't need assholes coming in here demanding things they can't afford to give. I don't like bullies."

Dani's eyes widened. She didn't even notice that Angel failed to answer *all* of her questions. "Me either! That's, like, why I want to learn how to take care of myself. You, like, can't possibly be around all the time. Some Viper chick is gunning for me, I think."

"Viper."

The way Angel said Viper's name caught Dani's attention. "You know her?"

"She's a recruiter. The Landlords have a rival. I call them the Pharmacy. Viper is their top runner. She's bad news, Kid."

"Yeah, well, she didn't look like she was part of the church choir. Why do you think I want to learn some stuff?"

Angel snickered at the Kid's sarcasm. "Some stuff. What you need to learn are skills to help you get out of here."

"I'm here, okay? I made my choice."

"A stupid choice," Angel barked. "You're just a kid. This isn't what you need or want for the rest of your life. This place," Angel spread her arms. "This place will eat you up, spit you out, then eat you up again. Do you have any idea how old Beard is?"

Dani shook her head.

"He's thirty-one. Been out here since he was about eighteen."

That couldn't be right. Beard looked like he was at *least* in his fifties. Maybe more. But if he's made it out here for this long, so could she, right?

"Don't even think about it, Kid. Beard is alive *only* because I got him off the shit he was hooked on. That's a constant battle for him. Sister helps, but he still struggles. That's what this place does to you. You hate your life so much that you will do drugs to get by. If you don't have money to score your dope, you sell. And I don't mean just drugs."

"I'm never going to sell myself!"

"Do you think Beard thought he'd do anything he's done out here? Come on, Kid. Wake up. This isn't the place for you."

"What about you? You seem fine."

Angel laughed mirthlessly. "You have no clue, Kid. I've been through worse than this. You are not me. You can't survive here. And you shouldn't have to." She could see the Kid's hackles going up. Good. She doesn't like being told she can't do something. Angel would use that to her advantage. "Let's make a deal."

Dani narrowed her eyes. "What kind of deal?"

"I'll teach you a few things *if* you take classes. Learn some skills that can get you out of here. Let Sister help you." Angel held up her hand when the kid opened her mouth — presumably to argue. "I know how old you are. I know *who* you are. And I know who Claire is."

Dani took a menacing step forward, her knife gripped tightly in her hand. "Are you threatening my girlfriend?" Before she even knew what happened, the knife was gone, and she was flat on her ass.

"It's good to know you still have some fire left in you when it comes to that girl. You're going to need it when you go crawling back to her one day, begging her for forgiveness. Do we have a deal?"

"Yeah, okay. Can I get up now?" Angel removed her boot from Dani's chest. "Do you think it's possible?"

"For you to get up? Sure. I went easy on you."

Dani rolled her eyes. "That Claire would forgive me."

"Do you think your love was true?"

Dani thought about Claire. About how she felt when Claire was near. How she felt now that she had lost Claire. "Yes. At least for me, it is. I think it was to her, too, but I hurt her."

"How do you think you could make it up to her?"

"By doing something right," Dani mumbled. "I'll go to the stupid classes."

"That's the spirit," Angel said dryly. "As promised, here's my first lesson. Don't come into these alleys alone anymore. Viper preys on the weak here, and she's very good at what she does. If intimidation doesn't work, she'll promise you anything you want. And she'll make good on one or two of those promises to suck you in. Don't get sucked in, Dani."

Dani's eyes widened. Angel was not kidding about knowing who she was. "I won't."

Chapter Ten

Claire yawned as she tried to get her key into the lock of her apartment. She was exhausted. School, an internship, and a paying job were kicking her ass. The only good thing about being too busy to breathe is it kept her from thinking about Dani. Most of the time. Okay, some of the time. Fine. She never stopped thinking about Dani, but at least she was too tired to do anything but grab a bite to eat and faceplant into her pillow for a dreamless sleep. Most of the time.

"Finally, geez. I'm starving!"

Claire gritted her teeth at her roommate. She rolled her eyes internally. *Girlfriend*, she reminded herself. "You know where the kitchen is, Cris," she mumbled irritably. The apartment was an absolute pigsty. Dishes littered the sink. Trash somehow missed the trashcan. There were five different glasses on the coffee table because, apparently, Cris didn't know how to use the same one. Before she had left that morning, Claire had cleaned up enough to satisfy the chaos in her head. After fourteen hours of being out, that chaos was back.

"Did you bring some food?" Cris shook a beer can, grumbling when it was empty.

"Did you *ask* me to bring some food?"

"No. I shouldn't have to ask you. Since you still have your shoes on, why don't you run out and get us a couple of burgers or something."

Claire spun on her heel, poised to say something she was possibly going to regret when her phone rang. "Hello?"

"That's some attitude to greet your mother with."

Claire sighed. "Sorry, Mom. It's been a long day. Any news?"

"I'm fine, dear." Karen could hear Claire grumble something and thought it best just to move on. "No, Claire Bear. I'm sorry. Honey, it's been nearly two years. How long will you keep searching?"

Forever. "I don't know."

"Babe, are you going to go get something or what?" Cris called out as she plopped herself back in her favorite spot on the couch.

"Claire, why is she still there?"

"Not now, Mom. I wasn't lying when I said it'd been a long day."

"Fine," Karen conceded. "But I'm just going to say one more thing."

I knew that was too easy, Claire thought. "Since when do you ever say just *one* more thing?"

"You're not too old to be bent over my knee and whupped, young lady."

For the first time that day, Claire chuckled. Her mom had never spanked her. Sure, there was the occasional threat, but that scared Claire enough to be good. "Say what you need to say, Mom. Apparently, I have to go get food."

"I get it, okay. She looked like Dani. Even I was charmed by Cris at first. But, honey, she's not Dani. Not even close. And you're running yourself ragged while she sits in your apartment, eats your food, and runs you ragged some more." Karen paused. "That sounded less dirty in my head."

"Mom!" Claire was glad no one was in the immediate vicinity to see her blush. "That was way more than one thing!"

"Fine. Stop torturing yourself, Claire. You're trying to convince yourself that you've moved on by dating someone you thought could have been another Dani. If you can tell me right now that you're happy, I will believe you and let it go. Are you happy, Claire?"

Claire opened her mouth to say yes. Then she saw Cris look at her incredulously, throwing her hands up in the air, then tapping her watch. "No. I have to go, Mom. I'll talk to you soon, okay?"

"I love you, Claire Bear. Dad says he loves you, too. He hasn't stopped looking. I wanted you to know that."

"Thank you. I love you both."

Claire pushed the end button and stood there for a moment. She thought about the day she met Cris. The way her heart had pounded a little harder. Her breath came a little faster. Her hope lit her soul. From a distance, Cris had looked like Dani. They had the same build, the same color hair, the same color eyes. She had run up to Cris, throwing her arms around her neck.

"Whoa! Not that I'm complaining, but do I know you?" Cris grinned at the pixie of a girl who was currently holding her tight.

Claire stepped back suddenly, embarrassed by her mistake. "I —I'm sorry. I thought you were someone else."

"I can be anyone you want me to be, cutie." She stuck her hand out. "Name's Cris."

"Claire," Claire offered, shaking Cris's hand. "I'm sorry again. I didn't mean to interrupt or cause any trouble." She saw those around them watching her with laughing eyes.

"No trouble. Can I buy you a drink or something?"

"No. Um, no thank you. I should . . ."

"Okay, how about you buy me a drink? Least you could do for practically assaulting me, right?" Cris gave Claire her best charming grin.

Claire tucked a strand of hair behind her ear. She hadn't even thought about being with anyone else since Dani disappeared. How could she? Her heart still belonged to Dani. But Dani left her. She hadn't heard a word from her ex-best friend/ex-girlfriend in nearly a year and a half. There was nothing to remain loyal to. Even though it felt wrong in her soul, she agreed. "Sure, okay."

Claire should have known then that Cris was a manipulator. Within two weeks, Cris had convinced Claire to let her move in with her. Oh, Cris had a silver tongue — in and out of bed — until lately. The sex had stopped, which didn't bother Claire as much as she thought it would have. The truth was, she still felt as though she was cheating on Dani each time she was with Cris. She was almost glad she didn't have to deal with that anymore. However, the pretty words had stopped as well. Anything about Cris that ever reminded Claire of Dani was gone. The colors were off. The charm had faded. And now Claire was left with the remnants of a dream she had wanted so desperately to make real.

"Hello?" Cris waved her hand in front of Claire's face. "You just gonna stand there or go get me some food?"

Claire's nostrils flared as she took a deep breath. "I'm just going to stand here," she answered. "*You*, however, are going to get your stuff and get out."

Cris frowned. No way she heard right. "What?"

"I want you out, Cris. Out of my home, out of my life."

"Come on, babe. You don't mean that." Cris grabbed Claire

by the waist and pulled her close. "You know you can't live without me and my tongue." She wiggled her eyebrows for effect.

"Believe me. I can. You're draining me. Not only of my money but my energy and happiness as well." Claire sighed when Cris let her go with a little push. "It's not all your fault."

"Not my fault at all!" Cris spat. "What the hell is this? You chase me, *beg* me to move in with you, and now you're kicking me out for no reason?"

"Wow. We really have different views of how this happened," Claire mumbled. "I didn't chase you, Cris."

"Oh yeah? Forget about the hug?"

"No. I told you then I thought you were someone else."

Cris snorted. "Yeah, I remember that line."

"It wasn't a line! I thought you were someone I lov . . . someone I once knew. And maybe it was wrong, but you looked so much like her that I allowed myself to get involved with you. The longer it went on, the harder it was for me to see that person anymore."

"So, you used me. Maybe *you* should be the one to move out."

"It's *my* apartment! And, yeah, maybe I did use you, but you sure got a lot out of it, didn't you. Free rent, free food, sex, not having to work. Now I'm done carrying you. And I'm done carrying this guilt around."

Claire held her breath as she waited for Cris's reaction. It wasn't that she was afraid of Cris. She still hated confrontation. Dani had helped her find a strength she didn't know she had. But Dani had also crushed her enough to crawl back into her shell. Crushed or not, she couldn't let this go on any longer.

"Where do you expect me to go? I gave up everything for you!"

"You didn't *have* anything, Cris! You were sleeping on friends' couches. Go back to that." Claire shrugged. "It's not my problem anymore."

"You mean *I'm* not your problem, right?"

Though it made her sound and feel like a bitch, she nodded. "Right."

"Your mom is going to be pissed at you. She effin' loves me."

"She's the one who told me to get you out of here!" Claire laughed. "Sorry, Cris, but your charm has worn off. I'm worn out."

"This is because of Bianca, isn't it? It was, like, one time, Claire!"

Claire shook her head. She had known about Cris's "indiscretion" with her ex. She also knew it was more than one time. And, yeah, maybe that should have been a huge factor in why she was breaking free now. In reality, that wasn't even in the top five.

"I don't care about Bianca, Cris. But since you brought her up, you can go live with her. That is if her girlfriend doesn't mind."

Cris stormed away, slamming the door of the bedroom open. Claire tried not to laugh when it hit the wall and came swinging back into Cris's face. There was probably damage on the wall, but Claire thought it was worth it as she followed.

"Those are mine," she said when Cris picked up her AirPods.

"Get another pair." Cris stuffed them in her bag and stomped to the dresser.

I don't think so. Claire went right behind Cris and took her AirPods back. Along with a few other things Cris figured she could get away with.

"Try sticking with your own stuff, Cris. I've done enough for you."

Cris's face twisted into fury. "You want this, too?" She threw a t-shirt at Claire. "I'm sure you bought that for me."

Claire tossed it back. "Nah, that has a stain on the front." She had a fleeting thought whether Dani would be proud of her. Then she forced it out of her head. Getting rid of Cris meant getting rid of Dani, too. It was time. Obviously, Dani wanted nothing to do with Claire, so Claire would focus on her future now instead of her past.

"When did you become such a bitch?" Cris spat.

"Around the time you ordered me to go get you food after I've had a long day of *working* and you've been sitting on your ass all day. Have everything? Because I'm tired and I want to take a shower and go to bed."

"It's been like ten minutes! Do you expect me to have everything I need to be packed up in that amount of time?"

Claire shuddered when she thought about how Dani packed for the "rest of her life" in ten minutes. "It's been done before."

CHAPTER ELEVEN

"Incoming!" Patty, the supervising nurse, was short in stature, yet when she spoke, people — even doctors — listened. "Pedestrian versus vehicle. Trauma room two! Page Dr. Vale!"

"We got a bad one, Patty. Is Vale on call?"

"Being paged now. Oh my, she's just a kid!"

"Yeah." The paramedic was just about to spout off his list of injuries when a tall woman in a white coat entered the room.

"What do we have?" Dr. Vale nodded at Patty before taking her place next to the patient.

"Severe lacerations on the head, torso, and arms. Legs." The EMT paused and swallowed hard. "One of the witnesses said whoever ran over her backed up and did it again." He lifted the bloody sheet revealing legs that had been mangled.

Dr. Vale swore under her breath. "Let's get her up to the OR stat! Do we have a name? Age?"

The paramedics looked at each other and shook their heads. "As far as we can tell, she's homeless. No one could give us a name. We picked her up on Skid Row."

"So young," Dr. Vale muttered. "Patty, send Mo up to the OR, please."

"Will do, Hunter. Now go. Help that poor child."

"I'll do my best."

Dr. Vale ran behind the gurney, hoping against hope that her best was good enough. She was one of the top trauma surgeons in the country. She prided herself on her abilities, her talents. Lately, the adrenaline rush she used to get working traumas has waned significantly. Now, however, with this young, broken girl on her table, Hunter Vale felt determined to do everything she could to keep her alive.

The clocked ticked over to hour number three, and a nurse dutifully wiped Dr. Vale's brow.

"I can't control this bleeding!" Dr. Mack worked vigorously to find the source of the blood pooling in the girl's opened abdomen.

"Keep looking," Hunter grunted. She was busy looking for a way to save at least *one* of the patient's legs but was quickly losing hope.

"Hunt, I could use you up here. I need another pair of hands. Another pair of eyes."

Hunter growled behind her surgical mask. "Get the saw and prepare the legs for amputation." She traded places with a resident who looked a bit in over his head. She would deal with that later. Hunter Vale needed only the best working for and with her. "The spleen needs to come out."

"I'll get to that. First, I need to find where the hell this blood is coming from."

"Blood pressure is dropping," the anesthesiologist announced.

"Working on it," Vale and Mack said together.

"Where are you, you little fucker," Hunter mumbled. "There's too much blood, Mack. Suction!" Her hands paused as the nurse did as asked. "Thanks, Mo. Keep it coming. Get some more blood in here!" she called out.

"If we don't get this soon, Hunt . . ."

"I know, Mack." Hunter also knew she was working on borrowed time. The bleeding wasn't their only complication. She needed to get back to the legs if she had any hope of salvaging anything above the knee. "Goddamn it! We need to remove the spleen." She glanced up at Mack. "Homeless. If she goes back out there without legs and a spleen . . ." Hunter didn't want to finish the thought.

"How does this country allow kids this age to be homeless?" Mack grumbled.

Hunter didn't answer. She knew if she started Mack down this road, he'd be ranting for days. Not that she disagreed with him, but she had more pressing matters at hand.

"There!" Hunter used her gloved finger to cover the nick she finally found. "Thoracic aorta. You got it, Mack?"

"Yeah." Mack cross-clamped the aorta. His surgical mask deflated and inflated with the deep breath he took. He looked over at one of the best surgeons he'd ever known. "Nice catch, thanks. I'm going to get a Foley catheter going here and take care of the rest. You work on the legs."

"I can't save them, Mack."

"All we can focus on now is saving *her*."

"Son of a bitch!" Hunter threw her surgical cap violently across the doctor's lounge.

"Hunt, there wasn't anything more you could do," Mo tried to soothe. She did, however, keep her distance from the irate doctor. They had grown up together — best friends since they were kids. Hunter's temper wasn't something she liked to mess with.

"What the hell was she doing out there on the streets, Mo?" It was a rhetorical question that she didn't expect an answer to. Besides, Mo wouldn't know. But *someone* out there had to have answers, and Hunter was determined to find out why in the hell this happened to this young girl.

"Hunt . . ."

"I just took the legs of someone who can't be more than eighteen years old, Mo. Her spleen is gone. Her insides are a fucking mess." Hunter ran her hands through her long black hair. Her blue eyes were rimmed red with fatigue and agony over decisions she had to make.

"I was in that OR, Hunter. What you did was save that girl's life. Honestly, I didn't think she would make it. Whoever did this to her," Mo shook her head. "I hope they caught the asshole."

"I don't know, but I'm going to find out."

"Hunt, it's dangerous in our line of work to get emotionally involved."

Hunter spun around and looked at Mo with anger. "You saw what I saw, Mo! You can't tell me you aren't as pissed as I am!"

"You're right. I am. But we've done everything we can for her. Now we let the police handle it."

"Come on!" Hunter threw her hands up in the air. "She's *homeless!* You think the police are going to put in the effort?"

"I'd like to hope so. Homeless or not, she's still human. A citizen of this city that was hurt on our streets."

Hunter scoffed. "Yeah, and the hospital will waive all charges for her. That's a *pipe* dream, Mo. That isn't how this world works."

"So you're going to get involved? Is that it?"

"Yes. I have to at least find out *who* she is. She's fucking listed as Jane Doe. What if there's someone out there who's missing her?"

"Fine. I don't like it, but I won't stand in your way. You're a big girl, and I'm sure you know what you're doing. But right now, we're going to go for some breakfast and calm down a bit."

Hunter scrubbed her weary face. "I'm not hungry."

"Well, I am. And I promised Patty I would stay with you and make sure you're okay. Are you going to make me go back to my wife and say I failed?"

Hunter sighed. "Fine. But only because I'm afraid of Patty. Though if you tell her that, you're dead to me."

Mo gave Hunter a half-hearted grin. The truth of the matter was, she *was* just as devastated by this case as Hunter was. But she couldn't risk her mental and emotional health in this line of business as hard as that was to do. Mo had a feeling, though, that Hunter was close to the end of her rope with her career.

"Man, *I'm* scared of that woman. Why do you think I'm practically begging you to take me up on my offer?"

"Are you paying?"

Mo snorted. "*You're* the surgeon! Come on. I know this great little place with some awesome pie! Even if you're not hungry, you can always eat pie."

Hunter's shiny RAM 1500 stood out among the tents and trash lining Skid Row. She shouldn't be here. It was probably the worst decision she had ever made as a doctor. To get personally involved. But she could remember the wails of sorrow coming from her patient earlier this morning, and Hunter made up her mind. "Jane Doe" wanted nothing to do with Hunter. She didn't blame the young girl for that. Hunter had irrevocably changed her life. It gave Hunter more of an incentive to find *something* that could help.

Besides, she hadn't been able to sleep. Mo's insistence that Hunter go out for breakfast with her had actually turned out really well. Not only had Hunter tasted the most incredible pie she'd ever had in her mouth, but she had also met the most beautiful woman she'd ever seen. Hunter had turned into a bumbling idiot, but from the time she met Ellie from Ellie's Diner, she nearly forgot the heartache she had caused the night before.

"Ya lost?" Beard gave the tall beauty an extra-long look. Hot or not, she didn't belong here. And people who didn't belong made Beard nervous.

"Uh, no. I'm trying to find some information." Hunter brought out her phone. She was likely breaking a ton of HIPAA laws, but she didn't care. She brought up a photo she had Patty take of their patient. "Do you know this girl?"

Beard took a step back. "Ain't no one tell ya that asking questions 'round 'ere ain't a good idea? You a cop?"

"I'm not a cop. I'm a doctor. This girl came into my ER last night, and I'm just trying to find out who she is. To *help!*"

Beard frowned. He didn't see the accident but heard it was terrible. He was sorry for the Kid, but rules were rules out here. You get seen as a snitch — even to a doctor — life gets a little harder.

"I can't help you, lady." He looked around to make sure no one was watching them. *Stupid*, he thought. Of course, people were watching. Fancy truck, fancy woman. Those things didn't belong here. "*Try the shelter*," he whispered, then shuffled off.

Hunter tried the shelter and was met with more unwillingness to help. Even the nun that worked there was reluctant, scared, or really didn't know much. If they did talk to her, they were asking for money. She should have thought to carry more cash. Then wondered if that would have been a good idea. In the end, she walked out of the shelter feeling frustrated, knowing nothing more than when she came here. To make matters worse, there was some hoodlum leaning against her truck.

"Can I help you?"

"No." Angel's arms were crossed, her hood low over her face. If anyone could see the scowl, they'd keep their distance. "Why are you here asking questions?"

Hunter frowned. The voice — unmistakably female — was rough. She figured the vocal cords had been damaged at some point. "I'm trying to help a patient."

Angel's posture relaxed — marginally. "Kid. How is she?"

"I can't . . ." Hunter sighed. "She's alive. That's all I can legally tell anyone who isn't family."

Angel scoffed. "We are her family. Look around you, Doc. We're all we have in the world."

"Yet, you call her Kid. I'm guessing that's not her real name. And no one is willing to help me with more information."

Angel pushed away from the truck. "Names are a liability out here. Knowing the who behind the why, getting emotionally involved in a Godforsaken place like this can be deadly. So can snitching or talking to people who don't belong here."

"Is that what happened to, uh, Kid?"

Angel considered the woman in front of her. She prided herself on being a good judge of character, and this woman seemed genuinely concerned for Angel's young friend. "Dani. Her name is Dani Reed. She recently turned eighteen."

"Dani," Hunter repeated. "How long has she been out here?"

"Too long," Angel answered.

"Runaway?"

Angel shook her head. "Kicked out because the mom didn't approve of her being a lesbian."

"You have to be shitting me!"

Angel smiled at Hunter's outrage. *She must be family.* "I wish I was. Dani has been out here for two years. She's kept to herself most of the time. Beard and Sister are her only 'friends,' so to speak."

"And you? Sounds like you know her pretty well. You must be pretty good friends."

"I — I helped her. Tried." Angel couldn't forgive herself for not being there in time to save Dani last night. When she had found out that Dani started working for Viper, Angel had been angry. She had wanted to teach Dani a lesson. The only thing Angel ever asked for was for those she helped to stay out of trouble and be kind to people. If they couldn't abide by that, they didn't deserve Angel's protection. Perhaps if Dani got roughed up a bit, she would remember who she really needed in her life and get rid of Viper and her merry band of drug assholes. But Angel never expected this. Expecting the unexpected was her job, and she had failed.

"What happened?" Hunter asked softly, sensing there was more to the story between this woman and Dani.

"Ask Dani." Angel turned to walk away.

"Wait! Please. She won't talk to me. Or anyone. What I had to do . . ." Hunter shook her head. "I just want to help her."

"You want to help? Keep her away from here. Don't let her come back."

"I can do more if I know more," Hunter tried again.

"What I've told you is enough. I will deal with who did this to her."

"Shouldn't you go to the police?"

Angel scoffed. "Shouldn't you? Or did you and they had nothing to say? Skid Row doesn't mean anything to people like them. People like you. We're not people. We're nuisances."

"Not to me."

"Because you feel guilty?" Angel guessed by the way the doctor was acting.

"Maybe that's part of it. Look, my name is Hunter Vale. I'm the head trauma surgeon at —"

"I don't need your resumé, doc. I told you the important

things about Dani and how to help her. Now, give me something more than she's alive."

Hunter took a deep breath. "You didn't hear this from me," she prefaced. "She had multiple internal injuries, a broken arm . . ."

"And?" Angel had seen her share of injuries. What she saw when she finally made it to Dani was one of the worst. Damn it! She should have been there! She should have gotten Dani out of the situation she was in the moment Angel found out about it.

"And," Hunter continued reluctantly. "I had to take her legs."

"Shit! Both?" Hunter nodded, and Angel fell back against the truck. "No wonder she isn't talking to anyone. She's had a problem with people bullying her because she's *different*. This probably makes things worse in her mind."

"Will she talk to you?"

"I can't . . . I'm sorry, but I can't go see her."

"Why?"

"Because I'm not the one she needs, doc. She needs to be rid of this place. *All* of it." *And I wasn't there to save her.* "She won't trust anyone in an authoritative position."

"What about Sister Haywood?"

Angel shook her head again. "I told you, no one from here. You keep her away, Dr. Hunter Vale. Do you understand? That's the deal here. None of this information came from anyone here. You got it from the police. As far as Dani is concerned, you were *never* here. Never met us." She took a menacing step towards Hunter. "Keep her away from here. It chewed her up and spat her out this time. Next time, it'll swallow her whole. She deserves better than this life. Find her better."

The woman in the hoodie stood toe to toe with Hunter, yet never looked up enough to give Hunter a clear view of her face.

"Will the fucker who ran over her be punished?" That wasn't what a doctor should want, but Hunter wanted it. Desperately.

"When I get all of the evidence I need that won't implicate Dani in any wrongdoing, yes."

Hunter's eyebrows shot up. "You'll go to the police?"

Angel chuckled. "I may be homeless, doc, but I'm a law-abiding citizen. Do you think we just kill people out here for the fun of it?"

"Someone tried to kill Dani. From what I was told, and the number of injuries Dani had, she was run over more than once."

Angel closed her eyes and said a small prayer for Dani. "They will be punished."

Hunter took the woman's word for it. She didn't know why, but she felt the hooded woman could be trusted. "I will do everything in my power to keep her from ending up back here," she promised. Hunter received a slight nod before the woman began to walk away. "The trauma to your vocal cords. Was it recent?"

Angel smiled but didn't turn back. "Not recent, doc. Don't worry about things you can't fix. Focus on what you can."

Chapter Twelve

Dani stared at the empty bed where her legs should be. It was real. The first time she woke up after surgery, Dani didn't believe it. *Couldn't* believe it. She thought maybe the drugs they had her on were messing with her mind. But each time she woke up from a med-induced sleep, she saw the same thing. Or, more accurately, she *didn't* see the same thing. No legs. How in the hell had her life come to this?

You got sucked in, she thought to herself. That was one thing she could remember. Dani couldn't, however, remember how she ended up here in this hospital bed, broken. The last thing she could recall was running drugs for Viper. Dani hated it. She hated that she had been weak enough to break a promise to Angel. But the money — what she saw of it — kept Dani fed. It got her socks and shoes. It *didn't* get her out of Skid Row like Viper promised, but it had been plenty for someone like Dani who had never had much most of her life.

Still, the thought that Dani had a part — however small — in ruining people's lives weighed heavily on her. People like Beard who tried so hard to stay clean with Angel's help. Dani was responsible for his relapse. No, Dani didn't sell the drugs to Beard. Nor did she personally hand them over to him. But she wasn't naïve anymore. She knew Viper slithered around Skid Row looking for those she could take advantage of.

It was when Beard nearly died that Dani decided she wanted out. No amount of money, food, or clothing was worth Beard's life. Or anyone else's. What if the drugs Dani ran ended up in some kid's hands? Hell, how did she know they hadn't already? Dani pretended she didn't know what was in the packages she delivered back and forth for Viper. It was her way of keeping her "innocence." But Dani was far from innocent. Far from stupid. And when she found Beard foaming at the mouth, she knew she was just as responsible as Viper was. So did Angel.

Dani looked at her nonexistent legs again. She tried moving her left arm, but the full cast prevented that. Oh, and the shattered bones didn't help, she supposed. Her chest hurt with each breath. Her head pounded like there was some percussion band up there. She felt . . . dead inside. And, yet, she was still freakin' alive. Why? Dani shook her head. She deserved this for what she did to Beard. Perhaps that's why Angel wasn't there to protect Dani when this happened.

It hurt to dwell on it. So, instead, she ate another cup of pudding — her seventh. They had pudding at the shelter. It was the same kind of pudding her dad used to stock up on at home. Chocolate, not the yucky vanilla crap. She didn't even think there was a natural ingredient in this little cup of sugary goodness. But it made her feel close to her dad, so she didn't care. Plus, Dani had a weakness for sweets. Maybe that's why she loved Claire so much. Her eyes began to water, and she forced herself to watch mindless TV to get over the sadness. *Yeah, like that's going to work.*

"Dani?"

Dani heard the voice of the doctor that took her legs. Someone she did *not* want to talk to. So, she ignored her as she usually did.

"There's someone I'd like you to meet," Dr. Vale said quietly.

Dani kept her eyes glued to the TV. She had no idea what she was watching, but anything was better than talking to some shrink or whatever. Even though she didn't invite anyone in, she could see from her peripheral that some blonde lady was coming towards her.

"If you're a shrink, I ain't interested."

The words came out harsher than she expected, but Dani didn't care. The people around here kept wanting her to talk about her problems. Like somehow that was going to make her freakin' legs grow back or something.

"I'm not a shrink, Dani. My name is Ellie Montgomery. I'm a friend of Hun — Dr. Vale's."

Dani's heart dropped. Dr. Vale. The one who did this to her. Why did Dr. Vale get to have friends when Dani had lost everything?

"Then I'm definitely not interested."

"Well, okay. If you don't want this apple pie . . ."

Dani's eyes flew to the lady. She hadn't had apple pie in, like, two years. *More* than two years. Heck, maybe since before her dad died. The lady held up a bag and swayed it back and forth enticingly. Dani couldn't help it. She wanted pie. And the lady looked kind enough. It helped that she wasn't a doctor.

"With ice cream?"

"The ice cream would have melted by the time I got here, but I'm sure we could rustle some up. I have friends in high places, you know," Ellie whispered conspiratorially.

She got closer to Dani's bed. It was almost comical how slow she was going in order not to spook Dani. What the hell was Dani going to do? Get up and run away?

"Nurse Patty?" A small smile played at Dani's lips. She liked

Nurse Patty. She sorta reminded Dani of Sister. Only a little older and sassier.

"Ah, so you know who the real bosses are here, huh?"

Ellie grinned and pressed Dani's call button. A couple of minutes later, the door opened, and a nurse waltzed in with a bored look on her face.

"What do you need?"

Dani sank back into her pillow. Nurse Iris. *Ugh.* Though the nurse looked nothing like Viper, their attitudes were twins. Or maybe Dani just thought of her as a snake. The point was, Dani didn't like her. At all.

"We need some ice cream," Ellie said pleasantly.

Dani didn't think this nurse deserved pleasant, but that's probably who this Ellie Montgomery person was. Why else would she be here talking to some teenager?

"Yeah, it's too late for that." Nurse Iris turned to leave without another word.

Rude, Dani thought. Somehow it made her feel better that it wasn't just her that the nurse was mean to.

"That's okay. I guess I'll just call Patty and see if she can bring us some," Ellie said.

Dani was impressed by how Nurse Patty's name stopped the redheaded nurse like she had a bungee cord attached to her ass. She was even more impressed when Ms. Montgomery pulled out her phone.

"I'll be back. We only have vanilla left," Nurse Iris snapped before storming out.

"Well, she's pleasant. Glad she didn't call my bluff."

Dani laughed at the face Ms. Montgomery made, then eyed

her suspiciously. "I thought you said you and Nurse Patty were friends."

"Oh, we are. But we just met about five minutes ago." Ellie shrugged. "I'm sure if I had a few more minutes, we would have exchanged numbers and become besties."

Ms. Montgomery gave Dani a cheeky grin that Dani couldn't help but chuckle at. The woman was nice and funny. But she was here because Dr. Vale asked her to be. That alone made Dani wary of her.

"What are you doing here?" Dani asked.

"Dr. Vale asked me to come and talk to you. I said okay."

"Why?"

"Why did she ask, or why did I say okay?"

Dani followed Ms. Montgomery as she sat in the chair next to Dani's bed. "Both, I guess," she answered finally.

Nurse Iris interrupted by barging in the room and slapping two small containers down on Dani's tray with a thud. "Here. Next time you use the call button, make sure it's for a good reason."

"Oh, I can assure you, ice cream is a *very* good reason," Ellie said seriously. "How else can we have apple pie a la mode?"

Nurse Iris narrowed her eyes to an annoyed squint, but that didn't faze Ms. Montgomery one bit. Dani supposed that was a check in the lady's pro side.

"Toodles," Ellie muttered and wiggled her fingers as the nurse stomped out the same way she had stomped in. "Do you have to put up with her every night?"

Dani shrugged. "She doesn't say anything to me, and I try not to bother anyone for anything." Dani's mouth snapped shut. *Idiot. You're falling into their trap.*

"I don't know," Ellie said quietly. "That's the answer to your question. I don't know why Hunter — Dr. Vale — asked *me* to come here. She's worried about you, and I guess that makes her desperate enough to try anything."

The answer sounded sincere to Dani, but she was still skeptical. No one helped unless they wanted something in return. "What do you get out of this?"

"The joy of your pleasant company."

The raised eyebrow was enough to make Dani shrink back an inch with a healthy dose of repentance. She watched silently as Ms. Montgomery opened the ice creams and the container she had brought in with her. It smelled heavenly. Though for the past two years, all Dani had smelled was shit and urine around her. Even the food at the shelter never smelled appetizing. The food was far better than digging scraps out of the trash, though.

"I hope you like apple," Ellie said as she slid the pie closer to Dani's good hand.

Dani nodded and shoveled a large bite into her mouth. She hadn't meant to be so impolite, but it smelled *delicious*. The taste, though? *Oh. My. God.* Never before had she put anything as amazing as this pie in her mouth. *Sorry, Claire.* Her eyes widened with intense bliss.

"Brain freeze?" Ellie asked.

Dani shook her head.

"Toothache?"

Another negative response.

Ellie smiled. "Good?"

Dani nodded vigorously. She shoveled in another bite before she even swallowed the first. Good lord, if she could eat this stuff for the rest of her life, she would die happy. Dani wondered if her new "friend" would give her more pie when she was back on the streets.

"I'm here, Dani, because I wanted to help you. Not just you, but Hunter, too. She feels such guilt for what she had to do, and you're not making it any easier."

The bite Dani just took was hard to swallow past the lump in her throat. "She took my legs." She couldn't hold back the anger and sorrow she felt.

"She saved your life."

"It would have been better if she had let me die," Dani argued, although there wasn't much fire behind the statement. It was kinda true, though. How was Dani supposed to manage being out on the streets when she had no legs? Yeah, Stump — he *made* people call him that — was out there. But the dude had been around for years and knew how to navigate the homeless world. It wasn't a disability to him. It was his way of life. Plus, it got him more dough when he panhandled. But Dani wasn't Stump. She wouldn't survive out there like this.

"How long have you been on your own?"

Dani's head shot up. How in the hell had this Ms. Montgomery person known? *Ask, idiot. Can't know the answers if you don't ask the questions.* "How did you . . .?"

"Hunter told me. She cares, Dani. Enough to find out about you in order to help you. How long?"

Dani was grateful for Dr. Vale's eagerness to help. But she was also confused as to how the doc even knew where to look. Maybe the cops or paramedics or whatever told Dr. Vale where Dani had been found? Dani couldn't dwell on that right now. This was a touchy subject to talk about. Could she get in trouble for running away at sixteen? Technically, she was forced out, but not many people believed teenagers. So, with fear coursing through her veins, she fibbed — just a little.

"A little over a year." Dani frowned with confusion. She had meant to say just a few months since she had turned eighteen. Eighteen was legally an adult, right? You couldn't get in trouble for running away at eighteen, could you? But, no. She had to tell this woman something closer to the truth.

"People tell me I'm easy to talk to," Ellie said with a small smile. "Maybe it's because I'm not threatening."

"Maybe it's the pie," Dani muttered. "You put something in here?" Tainted or not, she took another bite. And another.

"You caught me. It's called sugar."

Ms. Montgomery was so serious about her ridiculous answer that it broke Dani's scowl, and she smiled. "You're crazy."

"Ha! I'm actually the sane one." Tentatively, Ellie placed her hand over Dani's. "Talk to me. I promise you'll feel better. Keeping it all inside only creates a burden. But you don't have to carry it alone, Dani."

Dani felt herself *wanting* to talk. How could she? This woman wouldn't understand. She probably had a family who loved her unconditionally.

"I know what it's like to feel alone, Dani," Ellie continued when Dani remained silent. "To not have your parents on your side. I'm almost thirty-three years old, and I'm still afraid — every day — that my parents could destroy me just because they don't understand me."

Oh my god, she does *understand.* Hope — as small as it was — began to bloom in Dani's heart, and a tear rolled down her cheek. She nearly became a blubbering mess when Ellie reached up and brushed it away. The touch felt so motherly that it broke Dani's heart.

"My mom," Dani began. She had to stop and clear the lump from her throat. The fear she had inside was overwhelming. What if she told Ellie the truth, and she never saw her again? Dani had known Ellie all of fifteen minutes and yet the thought of Ellie turning away from her hurt. But maybe Ellie was right. Perhaps this burden was becoming too heavy for Dani to keep carrying alone. Lord knew what she was going to do once her stint in the hospital was over.

"I—I'm gay," Dani whispered, then waited for the outburst. The look of disgust. The rejection.

"Okay."

Huh? None of what she was waiting for happened. "You don't think I'm disgusting?"

"Oh, sweetheart, of course I don't."

Sweetheart. Dani let the endearment wash over her for a moment. "My mom does." Dani lowered her head. "After she saw me kissing my best friend — Claire — she gave me ten minutes to get out of her house. Told me that if my father were still alive, surely what I was would kill him. I was seventeen, Ms. Montgomery." *Sticking with the lie about your age, I suppose,* she chastised herself. As if she could get into any more trouble than she found herself in already. Dani lifted her big brown eyes to Ellie's. "I didn't have anywhere to go."

Ellie squeezed Dani's hand. "My friends call me Ellie. I'm so sorry that happened to you. What happened to Claire? Couldn't you stay with her?"

Dani shook her head. Just hearing Claire's name made her heart ache. "I loved her too much to put her through that. She offered, even begged me to stay with her, but I had — *have* — nothing to offer her. Especially now," Dani added, gesturing miserably to her missing legs.

"So, you made the decision for her."

Though Ellie's tone was gentle, Dani heard the disapproval. "I did what was best for her," she defended defiantly.

"Sweetheart, you took her choice away. Did Claire love you back?"

"I have no legs!" Dani shouted, avoiding the question.

"Is that the part of your body that meant the most to Claire?"

Unable to cope with her guilt for leaving Claire, Dani lashed out. "You don't understand! Just go away!" She tried pulling her hand away from Ellie's, but the small woman was stronger than she appeared.

"I understand more than you realize."

"Oh really?" Dani made a show of sitting up as much as she could to look at Ellie's legs. "Looks like you still have your legs. Stick with Dr. Vale, though. That could change!"

"That's enough!" Ellie leaned closer. "You want to blame someone for the loss of your legs, blame the driver that hit you. Or blame your mother for kicking you out when she should have hugged you closer." She put a hand over Dani's furiously beating heart. "But, *this* still beats, still lives, and can still love because Hunter made the *only* decision she could. The decision to save your life! This?" Ellie placed her hand on what was left of Dani's leg. "There is amazing technology out there that can help you walk again. You have that chance because of Dr. Vale. You have the chance to make things right with Claire because of Dr. Vale. And, you have the chance to prove to your mother that no matter what she does, she can't break you, because of Dr. Vale."

Dani dropped her head and sobbed. Not because Ellie yelled at her, but because everything she said was the hard truth. This wasn't Dr. Vale's fault. Dani could blame her mom or the driver, but in all reality, it was *her* fault.

When Ellie sat next to her on the bed and held her, rocked her, Dani pretended Ellie was her mother. She let the soothing words flow through her aching body. While it didn't help the physical pain, it did wonders for her emotionally. Why couldn't her own mother be like this?

"I — I'm homeless, Ellie," Dani hiccupped. "How am I supposed to support Claire? What if I'm too late, and she found someone else?" That thought made Dani cry harder.

"Oh, Dani." Ellie cupped Dani's face in her palms and rubbed away the tears with her thumbs. "Reach out to her. If it's too late, you do your best to move on. As far as supporting her, mutual love means mutual support. Claire wanted to help you before. Let her if she's willing. Needing help does not mean you're weak."

"Sure you're not a shrink?" Dani sniffled. Her lips twitched when Ellie laughed.

"I'm sure." Ellie dried more tears on Dani's cheeks. "Just a diner owner."

"And a baker." Dani reached around Ellie with her good arm to get another bite of pie. The ice cream melted, but Dani didn't care. "Ellie?" She looked up at Ellie through her long dark lashes. "I can't afford new legs."

Dani watched Ellie smile. Once again, she wished Ellie was her mother. Her smile was comforting and full of promise.

"Didn't I mention that I have friends in high places?"

Chapter Thirteen

"Ohmygodthisissogood." Dani took another mouthful of the most amazing fajitas she'd ever tasted. And she didn't just think that because she'd been on the streets for the last two years. These were seriously the *bomb*.

"I'm glad you're enjoying it," Ellie smiled. "But don't talk with your mouth full and wipe your chin."

Dani stopped chewing and gawked at Ellie. "You sound like a mother," she mumbled around the food.

"Sorry."

Dani swallowed and dutifully wiped her mouth. "No, don't be. It was nice being mothered again," she admitted quietly.

Ellie reached over and squeezed Dani's casted hand gently. "Did you have enough?"

Though she could probably eat a ton more, Dani resisted. "Mmm, yeah. I'm stuffed!" She let out a small burp and apologized with a bashful grin. "Thank you again for bringing me food. And, um, for, you know, visiting me and stuff."

"It's my pleasure, Dani." Ellie stood and began cleaning the remnants of food. "Are you tired, or would you like to talk for a bit?"

"Um, talk, maybe?" Dani picked at her cast nervously. The last time they had spoken, Dani had given Ellie what information she had on Claire. She hadn't dared to ask if Ellie had found out anything yet. And then there were the fajitas. Any person in their right mind would lose their train of thought while those things were around. But now the fajitas were gone, and Dani's belly was full — which may or may not be a good thing depending on Ellie's answer. No more stalling.

"You got it," Ellie smiled sweetly. She sat down in the cushioned chair and tucked her feet under her. "I found Claire."

Dani froze. The fajitas were fighting to make their way back up, and Dani swallowed hard. Was she sweating? She felt sweaty. Maybe she was coming down with something. She didn't want to get anyone sick. And by anyone, she meant Claire. No need to bring her here if Dani had pneumonia or something. *You're assuming she* wants *to come here to visit you.* Oh, god. What if Claire didn't want to see Dani?

"Dani? are you all right?" Ellie asked with concern.

Dani shook her head weakly. "Is . . . is she?" Ugh! Dani couldn't get her brain to work. She was definitely sick. Maybe it was worse than pneumonia. Like Ebola or something. She felt Ellie's fingers brush her hair out of her eyes, and Dani leaned into the motherly touch. If she didn't have Ebola brain, maybe she would have wondered if Ellie was a mother.

"She's still here in L.A.," Ellie answered, guessing Dani's question. "She's living in an apartment not too far from here."

Dani closed her eyes, trying to imagine what kind of apartment Claire would live in. What did she look like now?

"*Does she have someone,*" Dani whispered. The words physically hurt her, but she had to know.

"I don't know, sweets." Ellie eased herself onto the edge of Dani's bed. "I wanted to talk to you before I called her. I want you to make sure this is really what you want."

Is it? "What if — if she hates me? Or if she's in love with someone else?" Dani's head fell back onto her pillow. *Please don't let her be in love with someone else.*

"Do you want my opinion?" Dani nodded. "I think you owe it to *both* of you to see her again. She wanted to help you, and your pride kept you from letting her."

Dani's eyes popped open, but Ellie raised a finger to shush her.

"*If* she's with someone," Ellie continued. "Or if she decides she doesn't want to see you, at least both of you will have closure. I think if you don't do this, each of you will live with the 'what-ifs' for the rest of your lives."

Ellie was right, of course. *Dammit.* "Do you think she even remembers me?" It was a silly question, but one Dani asked herself many times in the past two years. Maybe it was her fear getting in her head. They were best friends for years before taking it to the next level. People don't just forget things like that. Do they?

"From the stories you've told me, I don't see how she could forget you." That got a small smile from the teen. "Give her a chance, Dani. it may not turn out the way you want, but at least you'll know."

Dani warred silently with herself. Not knowing if Claire was with someone or hated her, meant Dani could keep pretending they had a chance. But Ellie was right. Claire deserved better. It was time for Dani to stop letting her pride make decisions for her. Or at least try.

"Okay."

The anxiety in Dani's voice broke Ellie's heart. "Hey. No matter what happens, I'm here. I'm not going anywhere."

"Promise?"

Ellie smiled brightly. "I promise."

"Wait!"

Ellie's thumb moved away from the green call button. They had been doing this back and forth for the past ten minutes. Call. Don't call. Call. Don't call. Dani was eternally grateful for Ellie's patience as she was beginning to annoy herself.

"Sorry," Dani muttered miserably.

"It's okay. Take your time. If you decide you can't do this now, we can try another time."

"No! I mean, um, I want you to call. I need to know." Dani sighed. "Maybe you could, uh . . ." she glanced at the door hoping Ellie would get the hint.

"You want me to step out to call her?" Ellie guessed.

Dani nodded with relief. "Then maybe if she doesn't want to see me, you could break it to me gently? You seem like you'd be good at that."

Ellie chuckled. "Do I? Okay, if it makes you feel better, I'll go out into the hall. Don't go anywhere. I'll be right back."

Dani snorted with laughter. She appreciated that Ellie could joke with her. It made her feel normal. It was never over the top or cruel with Ellie. The teasing was gentle and fun. Dani found herself really warming up to the woman. She may have lost the love of her mother and her legs, but talking to Ellie the past few days has helped a lot. And now there was even a small chance of getting Claire back.

"Well, I was thinking about going for a stroll, but I guess I can stick around for a while," Dani grinned.

"You do that." Ellie gave her a wink and stepped out of the room.

"Now I wait," Dani said to herself. She was never good at waiting. If she could pace, she would. Hell, if she could bounce her leg, she would. But she could only lay there . . . and drum her fingers on her good hand.

Claire flipped her grilled cheese. "Perfect," she said to herself. She had been doing that a lot lately. Talking to herself. Ever since Cris left, Claire had been feeling better about herself. Yeah, she may be a little lonely, but it was better than dealing with a manipulator like Cris. Now, when Claire was tired, she could come home, take a bath, and go to bed. She didn't have to worry about making sure Cris was fed. Or satisfied. Claire rolled her eyes. Sex wasn't *that* important.

She opened the fridge and eyed the Diet Coke for a long moment. Grilled cheese and ramen weren't the healthiest selections, so Claire opted to balance it out with a bottle of water. Her mom would be appalled. But Claire simply couldn't find the motivation to cook decent meals for herself. Especially on the days she did her internship at the publishing company. Those days were the hardest — and best.

Going to classes was fun for her now. Nothing like it was in high school. While Claire's grades had always been immaculate

— she didn't count the last couple of months of her senior year after Dani disappeared — she never really enjoyed herself. School was mostly about who you were dating, what you were wearing, or if you were popular.

In college, you got to choose what you wanted to focus your energy on. Friends weren't high on Claire's list. She tended to keep a low profile and work hard for what she wanted. That included trying to get her master's degree in writing with a concentration in publishing. It wasn't easy for Claire; she was crap at writing. But she loved to read. She loved everything about books. They took her away from the harsh world she had to live in. They allowed her to become someone else and forget that her heart was most likely lost forever.

Lesbian authors writing lesbian fiction. *That's* what Claire loved. That's what she wanted more of in the world. So, Claire had a plan. She would work hard in school, start in the mailroom of a publishing company if she had to, become an editor, and eventually, she would own her own publishing company. Claire knew the road ahead might be a tough one, but she was ready for it.

She picked up her copy of the new Joselyn Cohan novel — hot off the presses. One of the benefits of interning at her favorite author's publishing company. Claire had just started the book, but she could already tell she was going to love it. Books like this solidified why Claire chose the profession she did. She wanted to make more books like this for girls like her to enjoy. A little romance, a little mystery, and badass women who save the day. Who wouldn't love this stuff?

The shrill of her phone made Claire jump and nearly dump everything she had in her hands. She had just spoken to her mother, so it wouldn't be her. And Claire had no real friends. At least no one that would call her at this time of night just to chat. She glanced at her perfect grilled cheese sandwich, her steaming soup, and her waiting book, and considered ignoring the call. But something inside her told her to pick up.

"Hello?"

"Hello, I'm looking for Claire Oliver."

Claire frowned at the pleasant female voice on the other end. She held the phone out to look at the number. It was local, but she didn't recognize it.

"This is she," Claire answered cautiously.

"My name is Ellie Montgomery. I'm calling to speak to you about Dani Reed. Please hear me out before you hang up."

Claire's heart nearly leaped out of her chest. Hadn't she just vowed to get over Dani? And it had been working — sort of. At least Claire hadn't been thinking of Dani twenty-four seven. Only when she was awake. Or when she was dreaming.

"I — I'm not going to hang up. Is Dani okay?" Claire's voice wavered when she said Dani's name. *Yep, totally over her.* "Do you know where she is? Have you seen her?" This was her first lead in two years!

"She's . . . yes, I've seen her. She gave me your name and asked me to call you."

Jealousy's green tentacles began to wrap around Claire's heart. "How? I haven't heard from her in so long; I thought she had forgotten about me." Unfortunately, she couldn't hold back the bitterness in her voice. "Everything has changed."

"Have your feelings changed?"

"Who the hell are you? What do you know about my feelings!"

"Claire, Dani is in the hospital."

"*Oh my God.*"

"I can't tell you she's okay," Ellie continued. "But she's alive. And, she has asked for you."

Dani was in the hospital. Claire heard that phrase over and over in her head. This was something she had feared for the past two years. The streets were no place for a teenager. Hell, it was no place for *anyone*. But Dani was never as tough as she pretended to be. She had a soft heart. What if she got into drugs? Or worse?

"Why me?"

"Because her feelings haven't changed, Claire. She still loves you."

Tears began to flow freely down Claire's cheeks. "Did she love me when she told me to get away from her?" she cried. "Did she love me when she pushed me away as I begged her to let me help?"

"Yes," Ellie answered firmly. "She thought she was doing the right thing. She felt she had nothing to offer you, and thought you needed more than a failure like her."

"She is *not* a failure!" Claire yelled. "It wasn't her fault her mother was a fucking bitch!" She didn't know who this lady was, but Claire was ready to throw down to defend Dani.

"Claire," Ellie prompted quietly. "I agree with you. And I've told Dani the same thing, in less colorful language." She smiled at Claire's soft giggle. With a deep breath, Ellie continued. "Her situation has gotten worse, and she could use a friend."

"Worse how?" Claire asked timidly. What could be worse than being on the streets at sixteen?

"I'd rather tell you that face to face," Ellie suggested carefully.

Claire struggled with what to do. "I don't know," she said softly. The tears wouldn't stop. "It took me a really long time to get over Dani pushing me away." *I'm still not over it.* "I don't know if I can go through that again. I barely survived the first time."

"Do you still love her, Claire?"

The voice on the other end of the line was soft and caring. Claire could feel the warmth as though they were in the same room. Perhaps that's why Claire was able to be honest with this Ellie Montgomery person.

"I — I never stopped. I tried. God, I tried, but I couldn't get her out of my heart." Claire sniffled. *"I looked for her."*

"She wasn't ready to be found, sweetheart. The rejection from her mother destroyed her. I don't agree with what she did to you, and I've told her that. I think she understands now. Claire, she needs you."

"Who are you to Dani?" Claire asked. If the woman was trying to reunite Claire and Dani, surely she wasn't a threat. But that didn't mean Claire wasn't still a little jealous that Dani had been so open with her. "Why is she opening up to you? Are you a doctor?"

"No, I'm not a doctor. Actually, I'm a friend of Dani's doctor who asked me to come in and speak with Dani. She just needed a friend. But now she needs someone more."

Claire wasn't buying it. Dani didn't just open up to people. "But, you must be someone special if Dani opened up to you," Claire tried again.

"It was the pie," Ellie said with a chuckle. "I brought her pie, and I guess she felt like she could trust me."

Claire laughed. "That would do it. Dani has always been a sucker for sweets." She let out a long, weary sigh. "Where is she?"

"You'll come see her?"

"Yes. How can I stay away? She still owns my heart."

Chapter Fourteen

Claire watched a woman pacing in front of the hospital entrance. She was a petite, beautiful woman, and Claire's earlier jealousy reared its ugly head again. The woman looked older than Dani, but that didn't mean much these days. Age was nothing but a number. Claire shook her head. If this was Ellie Montgomery, Claire owed her more than some stupid jealousy. Dani was about to be back in Claire's life because of this woman. Claire needed to focus on that. And on not chickening out. She was so nervous!

"Excuse me?"

Ellie spun around. "Claire?"

Claire nodded. "Miss Montgomery?"

"Ellie." Ellie held her hand out and felt the slight tremor in Claire's. "How are you?"

"Nervous as hell," Claire answered honestly with a shaky smile.

"So is Dani." Ellie gave Claire a charming smile hoping it would help calm Claire's nerves.

For some reason, knowing Dani was nervous caused Claire to grin. She released Ellie's hand and ran hers through her hair. Funny, she was anxious about what Dani would think about her hair. It had been long the last time they saw each other. Dani had always liked it long. "*Something to hold onto,*" Dani would say. The pixie cut was a drastic change.

Claire took a deep breath. "I'm sorry I'm late. I — I couldn't quite make my legs work. I hope you haven't been waiting out here long."

Ellie's smile faltered slightly, but she didn't think Claire noticed. Having to tell Claire about Dani's legs is what Ellie dreaded the most. "It's okay. I used the time to take a walk. Dani was about to drive me crazy." Ellie laughed, relieved when Claire laughed with her.

"She can be headstrong, that's for sure," Claire agreed wholeheartedly.

"Oh, you're being nice!" *It's time, Ellie.* Ellie's heart beat a little faster, but she was determined to be strong for both Claire and Dani. "Claire, there's something you should know before we go up to see Dani."

"Whatever it is, I don't care. I just want her in my life again." Claire paused in her declaration. "Wait. Please tell me she's not dying. I figured she's been on the streets for a while. Did she — has she had to do things?"

Images of Dani as a drug addict or prostituting consistently entered Claire's mind. No matter how much she tried to force herself to have happy dreams about unicorns, her unconscious said, "nope."

"She's not dying," Ellie assured immediately. "Anything else you need to know about her time out there, she'll have to tell you." Claire nodded. "And, I know you're anxious to see her, but you need to hear me out. Okay?"

"Okay."

For reasons Claire didn't understand, she felt deep down that whatever she was about to learn was going to devastate her. *I can be strong.*

"Dani was involved in an accident."

Claire immediately began to cry. She readily accepted Ellie's comforting touch.

"She was hit while crossing the street," Ellie continued. "I won't lie to you, Claire. It's bad."

"W—what happened to her?" Part of Claire wanted to stick her fingers in her ears like she did when she was a little girl. If she didn't hear the news, it didn't happen. But that's not how the real world — the adult world — worked. So, she listened. She may be sobbing uncontrollably already, but she was listening.

Ellie pulled the girl close and held her tight before giving her the news. "She's pretty banged up," she began softly. If she could ease Claire into this, it would be better. Ellie nearly scoffed at herself for that thought. *How will hearing this news about someone you love* ever *be easy?* Even so, she continued with the lesser injuries. "Dani has a broken arm, a few broken ribs, and some internal damage that was addressed during surgery."

Since Ellie wasn't a doctor, she relied on what Dani had told her and what Dani allowed Hunter to say in front of Ellie. She didn't understand everything that was said about the surgery, so she stuck with generalizations.

Claire took a shallow breath. A broken arm and ribs, she repeated in her head. That wasn't too bad. She was sure Dani was hurting, but that would heal. *There's more.* Another feeling of dread washed over her.

"What else?" Claire managed. "None of what you told me needed to be said before seeing her, so there's something you haven't told me. Something bad. She obviously remembers me since she told you about me. That means no major head trauma." Claire looked up at Ellie — who wasn't much taller than Claire. Perhaps Dani's height if she stood up straight.

Ellie nodded. *Smart girl.* "You're right." Ellie sighed. "Claire, in order to save Dani's life, they had to . . . amputate her legs."

Oh, God! Whatever Claire conjured up in her head disappeared and was now replaced with trying to imagine her best friend, the person she loved, without legs. *Be strong,* she reminded herself. Unfortunately, Claire didn't know if she was that strong. The fear that she wasn't strong enough intensified when she broke down. She allowed Ellie to comfort her. Claire needed her mother right now, but somehow Ellie filled that role. For now.

Claire blew her nose with the tissue Ellie gave her and sniffled. *Enough of this. It has been two years. It's time.* "Can I see her now?"

"Of course. Why don't you go and splash some water on your face, and then I'll take you up to see her."

Claire mindlessly followed Ellie to the bathroom, grateful when she was left alone. The cold water felt icy on her hot face. The shock of it brought Claire out of her haze. She looked at herself in the mirror. "You can do this. Dani must be scared. You're going to forget the last two years, go into that room, and this time you're going to help her. Whether she likes it or not."

Dani's nonexistent legs itched. Was that even possible? It was like they wanted to get up, move around. Dani had to remind herself that *they* weren't there anymore, so *they* had no say in anything anymore. But that didn't stop them from "itching."

What the hell is taking so long? Son of a bitch! Dani had never been so damned scared in her life. She lived on Skid Row for freak's sake, but *this* was far scarier than that. What if Claire was pissed at her? God, what if she pitied her? Or worse, what if Claire didn't love her anymore?

"*Closure*," Dani whispered in the empty room. Isn't that what Ellie said? If nothing else, at least Dani would know where she stood with Claire after the night was over. She laughed sarcastically and rolled her eyes at the thought of standing at all. The light knock on the door caused Dani to gasp and nearly choke on her own spit.

"Yeah?" she managed once she stopped coughing.

Ellie poked her head in, immediately sensing Dani's angst. "Are you ready for some company?" she asked brightly. Dani nodded weakly. "*It's okay*," Ellie mouthed and opened the door wider.

The moment Claire walked in that room, time seemed to stop. Both girls began to cry immediately. Claire ran to Dani's bedside, and after a split-second hesitation, she launched herself at Dani.

"Why didn't you let me help you? Why didn't you stay with me?" Claire sobbed while kissing Dani's stunned face.

Dani used her good arm to hold Claire as tightly as she could. She didn't want to let go. Ever. "I was stupid," she readily confessed. "Forgive me, baby. Please? I have nothing to offer you . . ."

"You!" Claire stated angrily. "All I ever needed was you!"

Dani tenderly wiped tears from Claire's cheek. "*I need you,*" she whispered.

Claire heard the click of the door, and she turned to see Ellie had given them their privacy. There was so much she wanted to say — questions she wanted to ask. But right now, she just wanted to be with Dani. She had wanted to *be* with Dani for two years but wasn't allowed that chance. As excruciating as it was seeing Dani so broken, Claire couldn't get past the anger and hurt of being left behind.

Dani noticed immediately when Claire's demeanor changed. It was something Dani learned when they were kids. When Claire was upset, she would start to withdraw. Sometimes Dani would wish that Claire would just yell about what Dani did wrong. And maybe throw things because Dani thought seeing that side of Claire would be cute. But Dani usually had to guess what she did wrong, which was never a good thing. It would always end with Claire being pissed about something totally different than what she was already pissed about.

"Do you want me to get Ellie to come back in?" Dani asked cautiously.

Claire eased away and sat in the chair next to Dani's bed. "Is that what you want?"

"What I *want* is for this awkwardness to go away. Was it just an act? Cuz, when we had an audience, you seemed happy to see me. Now it kinda feels like you don't wanna be around me."

Claire reined in her annoyance. "Did you expect everything to be okay, Dani? That I would walk in here and forget the past two years?"

Dani glanced towards the door. "I — I told Ellie it was only a year." That wasn't what she freakin' wanted to say. An actual answer from Claire threw her for a loop. She would like to have blamed the stupidity on her head injury, but nah. She was stupid way before the accident.

"*That* is what you're worried about?" Claire asked incredulously.

Oh boy. Is it too late to change my mind about wanting Claire to yell? Dani scrubbed her good hand over her face. "No. I . . ." She took a deep breath. "I don't know what to say," Dani admitted after a long pause.

"Neither do I." Claire sighed. Part of her felt like a dick for being upset. Dani had been through a lot at her young age. But that was part of the problem. This could have been prevented if Dani had just let Claire help. "Let's forget about the past for a minute and talk about the future."

Dani's head fell back onto the pillow. *What future?*

"What are you planning on doing after you get out of here? Where will you go?" Claire continued when Dani said nothing.

She doesn't want me. I should have known. Who the fuck would want someone with no freakin' legs? "I dunno," Dani muttered.

She still can't ask me for help, Claire thought miserably. "Dani, look at me." She waited until Dani's eyes met hers. "I'm here. Don't run away again. Let me help you."

It took almost a full minute, but Dani finally nodded. "Yeah, okay. I, uh, meant it when I said I needed you. I don't think I could survive . . ." Dani had to swallow the lump in her throat.

"Wait, I'm not asking you to let me help because I don't think you could survive on the streets like this, Dani. I'm asking because I love you."

Dani reached out for Claire's hand, smiling when she readily took it. "I was going to say I don't think I could survive without you again."

Claire willed away the tears that threatened. "We have a lot to talk about. You understand that, right?"

"Yeah. But for now, can we just, I don't know, be together?"

Claire nodded. "For now." She scooted forward in her chair, getting closer. "You're going to come home with me when you get out of here, right?"

"I — I can't pay rent. At least not yet."

"I don't care about that, Dani. I care about you."

"*I* care."

"You are so frustrating!" Claire laughed. She had to. If she didn't, she'd be pulling her hair out. Or Dani's. "How about this? We deal with things one day at a time. Right now, you're stuck in here for however long. I need to make arrangements with work and stuff to be here as often as I can."

"Claire . . ."

"That's not up for discussion," Claire interrupted. "So, Ellie? She's friends with your doctor?" Dani nodded. "I wonder if she could hook me up with a more comfortable seat in here."

"I'm, uh, sure Nurse Patty can." Dani was reeling. Claire wanted to be with her. Like, literally *be* with her here in the hospital. She couldn't believe how lucky she was that Claire still loved her.

Claire made a mental note to find Nurse Patty. She caught Dani trying to stifle a yawn and mentally kicked herself for not being more sensitive to Dani's well-being. "Are you tired?'

"No," Dani yawned, then snickered. "I get tired pretty easily, don't take it personally. It's definitely not the company," she winked.

Claire grinned. "I hope not because you're stuck with me." She stood and took it upon herself to lower the head of Dani's bed.

"What are you doing?"

"Tucking you in. You need to rest."

"But . . ."

"But nothing. I'm going to go find this Nurse Patty and see what rules I can break by being here."

"Claire Oliver, you've never broken the rules!" Dani teased.

"Things change," Claire countered. She hadn't meant for it to sound so serious. *It is what it is*, she thought. And what it was, was the truth.

Of course, Dani caught the true meaning of what Claire said. Circumstances change the course of a person's life — good or bad. They had spent two years apart. And while Dani was grateful for the reprieve Claire was allowing her, Dani knew at some point her actions that tore them apart would come back to bite her in the ass. Until then . . .

"Like your hair?" Dani smiled.

Claire's hand self-consciously went to her short hair. "Uh, yeah."

"I like it. A lot."

Claire blew out a relieved breath. "Good. Now, I'm going to step out for a moment, but I'll be right back."

"I could just push the call button," Dani suggested.

"No, that's okay. I need to use the restroom, anyway."

Dani pointed to a door in her room. "I got the fancy accommodations," she grinned cheekily.

Claire forced a giggle. She needed a moment to herself but hadn't wanted to make Dani feel bad by telling her that. The excuses were weak. True, but weak. "What you don't have are snacks. And I didn't get to eat my grilled cheese. Which was cooked perfectly, I might add."

Dani's face fell. "You left a grilled cheese sandwich? How? Why?" She shook her head. "You could have scarfed it down on the way over here!"

Claire raised a brow. "Do you think that's what I was thinking about when some strange lady called me and told me my . . ."

"Girlfriend?" Dani suggested when Claire hit a snag during her little speech.

"My *girlfriend*," Claire emphasized, picking up where she left off. "Was in the hospital and asking for me?"

Dani gestured at her legs. "It's not like I'm going anywhere. You could have totally eaten that sandwich first."

Claire gave Dani a half-smile. She wasn't sure if she wanted to laugh or cry at Dani's joke. "Well, it doesn't matter. I'm here now, and the sandwich is no longer ooey-gooey goodness." She leaned down and gave Dani a quick kiss on the cheek. "I'll be right back, okay?"

Dani grinned. "'Kay. I'll be right here," she said sleepily.

Claire gave Dani's shoulder a quick, light squeeze before leaving the room. Once outside the door, she slumped back on the wall and began to sob. She covered her mouth with her hand, not wanting Dani to hear her. She had hoped she'd make it to a nearby bathroom before breaking down, but she was lucky to have made it out of the room.

"Claire?"

Claire gasped, quickly wiping the tears away. "Miss Montgomery, er, I mean Ellie. I, uh, was just going to get some snacks, and, um," she sniffled. "I hoped to find a Nurse Patty. I wanted to talk to her about . . ."

She knew she was talking fast. Claire usually did that when she was nervous or embarrassed. Right now, she was both. The compassionate look on Ellie's face, however, caused Claire to lose it all over again.

Ellie immediately took Claire in her arms and held her. "It's okay. I'm here." She rubbed Claire's back with a motherly touch. "Did something happen?"

Claire shook her head. Then nodded. Then shrugged. "I don't know what I'm doing, Ellie. What if I can't keep it together when I'm with Dani? I need to be strong for her, but seeing what happened to her hurts so bad. I know that sounds selfish."

"No, that sounds like you love her." Ellie nudged Claire until they were eye to eye. "You don't need to be strong for her every second of every day. In fact, I think it would be better for both of you if you were honest about how you felt. If you're scared, tell Dani. If you're sad, tell her. Odds are, she's feeling the same way."

"Really?"

Ellie's heart broke for the young woman. She had a long, hard road ahead of her. Perhaps it wasn't fair to ask someone so young to put her life on the back burner practically.

"Really," Ellie insisted. "But, Claire, if you're not up for this, no one will blame you if you walk away right now."

Claire shook her head emphatically. "I would blame me. Dani walked away from me, and it nearly broke me. It *did* break her. I won't do that to her. To either of us." She wiped away the remnants of her tears. "I may be young, but I'm not naïve. I know that this isn't going to be easy. But it's going to be a hell of a lot easier for me than it will for Dani." Claire sighed. "Maybe I'm fooling myself. Or maybe it'll hit me later just how difficult this will be, but I'm still not going anywhere."

"Neither am I," Ellie promised. "Got it?"

Claire sniffled again and nodded. "Thank you. Do you, um, know Nurse Patty?"

Ellie smiled. "I do."

"Maybe you could help me convince her to put a more comfortable chair in Dani's room for me? And, like, let me stay?"

"I think we can do that. Come on." They walked down the hall, arm in arm. "About those snacks. I'll let you get away with vending machine stuff today, but I will bring you better food tomorrow."

"You don't have to do that."

"I know." Ellie hip-checked Claire.

Claire genuinely laughed for the first time since receiving the call earlier that evening. She stopped abruptly. "I have to call my parents!"

"Okay, we can take care of that after . . ."

"No, you don't understand. My dad still looks for Dani every night. He's probably out there right now! Oh my God, they're going to be so happy!" Claire frowned. "And sad. Ugh. Do I tell them what happened on the phone or in-person?"

"Well," Ellie started cautiously. "If it were me, I would appreciate being told in person. But if I were you, I would go see them instead of having them come here. I'm assuming they live close by."

"Yeah. And you're right. I should go there." Claire took a deep breath and blew it out. "I'm going to have to quit my internship. Maybe my job if I can't get a more flexible schedule. And my classes . . ."

"Hey," Ellie interrupted softly. "You don't need to give up anything. Dani has all the help she needs while she's here. When she goes home, we'll help you work out a schedule so that you can keep doing what you need to do for yourself."

Claire was skeptical that she'd be able to juggle so much. She was already having a hard time with her schedule. "Why are you helping us?"

Ellie took no offense with the question. It wasn't often strangers got so involved in other people's lives. "Because I know what it's like to feel hopeless. Someone helped me, and it changed my life."

"The person that helped you. Do you still talk to them?" Claire asked. She wondered if Ellie would be gone once Dani got out of the hospital. She didn't think Dani would like that. It didn't take long to see Dani had already formed a bond with the woman. She didn't need another mother figure walking away from her.

Ellie smiled brightly. "She's my best friend. I couldn't imagine life without her. You'll meet her soon, I'm sure."

Relief flooded Claire's heart. "I can't wait!"

"Now that you're satisfied that I'm not going to leave Dani like her mother did, let's go talk to Patty."

Claire cringed. "You knew, huh?"

Ellie nodded. "I don't blame you. Dani didn't deserve what happened to her. You have a lot to worry about, Claire. My leaving is not one of them. Okay?"

"Okay."

Chapter Fifteen

"Mom?"

Claire peeked in the house before coming in. Part of her hoped no one was home. The other part wanted to get this over with. She had been rehearsing what she was going to say to her parents all the way here. None of the words Claire came up with sounded right. But Dani would be released soon. Hunter and some of her friends had been in and out of Claire's apartment, getting it ready for Dani's wheelchair. Appointments for physical therapy and prosthetic fittings were being made. It was all very real now. She couldn't keep her parents in the dark anymore. For one, they deserved to know what happened. And second, Claire was going to need their help.

"In here!" Karen called out from the kitchen.

Claire took a deep breath, closing the door behind her. *Here goes nothing,* she thought as she slowly made her way to her mom.

"Hey."

"Hey! This is a surprise. We didn't expect you until the weekend." Karen hugged her daughter, sensing the tension. "You've been so busy lately; I was beginning to wonder if weekend dinners were going to get cut. Or is that why you're here?"

"No. I mean, I don't know." Claire ignored her mom's look of concern and stole a french fry from the tray her mom just took out of the oven. That must mean her dad is here or close to home. "French fries? What happened to eating healthy?"

"Potatoes are good for you," Karen countered with feigned grumpiness. "What's going on, Claire Bear?"

"Can we wait until Dad is here?"

Karen sat down with a thump. "It must be serious. Is Cris back?"

Claire shook her head. "No, Mom. I learned my lesson with her. I should have listened to you."

"I'm just glad it's over now. But . . ."

"Mom."

"Fine, we'll wait for your father. But you need to stop eating the fries. They'll be gone before he can have any."

"You'll just have to make more," Claire grinned as she popped another one in her mouth.

"Would you like a burger, too?"

"Nah, I'm not hungry," Claire replied with her mouth full of yet another french fry.

"Clearly." Karen shook her head and put another patty in the skillet. "Do you want to give me a hint as to why you're here?"

"Nope." Just then, Claire heard the front door open. She hopped up and ran to greet her dad.

"Well! Hey there, sweetheart! This is a surprise!" Jose accepted Claire's enthusiastic hug with joy. An unscheduled visit from his "very busy" daughter was rare. He looked over her shoulder to his wife. *What's going on?* He mouthed. Karen shrugged, gesturing for him to come into the kitchen.

"Dinner is ready. Claire, do you want to get the plates?" Karen set a platter on the table and eyed her husband. Both knew something big was going on for Claire to be here. "How is the internship going?" she asked Claire as she helped set the table.

"Great!" *Even though I may have to quit.* "I'm reading the new Joselyn Cohan book as one of my assignments."

"Oh! That's your favorite author, right?"

"Yeah. The book is amazing so far. I have to finish it soon, though, and things have been a little crazy." *Great segue, Claire.*

"I keep telling you you're taking on too much, Claire Bear." Jose thanked his wife for the plate full of a burger and fries she handed him. "School is hard enough. Throw in a job and internship . . ."

"Dad, please."

"I'm sorry, hon. But I worry about you. That's what parents do."

"*Not all parents,*" Claire muttered moodily. "I can't believe Rita got away with what she did to Dani."

"She didn't exactly get away with it, Claire Bear," Jose reminded his daughter.

"A fine and probation? Come on, Dad. Dani was out on the streets for two years. Two. Years! Rita is making payments on her fine. How is that any kind of punishment for kicking your kid out?"

"I agree with you, sweetheart, but . . ."

"You said if Dani was hurt while out there, Rita could be charged with a felony, right?"

"Yes," Jose answered carefully. Rita had moved away a little over a year ago. He thought keeping Rita out of Dani's life was the best course, especially *if* Dani was hurt. She wasn't going to need or want to fight her mother, too.

"Is there some sort of limitation on that?" Claire wondered.

"Like a statute?" Claire nodded her response. "Well, I'm not sure. Dani is eighteen now, Claire Bear. She's a legal adult." Jose glanced at his wife before giving Claire his attention again. "Why do you ask?"

Claire tapped a fry on her plate. "I found Dani," she revealed quietly. "Or, technically, she found me."

The utter silence in the room was unnerving. Claire had expected to be bombarded with questions. Instead, her parents merely stared at her.

"Did you hear me?"

"Yes," Karen answered first. "We're waiting for more information, Claire. Your father has been looking for Dani every night since Rita kicked her out. Now you're here, calmly telling us that you've found her as though it was a normal conversation."

"And asking about statutes of limitations," Jose interjected. "Was Dani hurt?"

"Okay," Claire took a breath. "I got a call from this lady not too long ago . . ."

"How long ago?" Karen asked briskly.

"Honey, let her explain," Jose soothed. He had gone out the night before, searching Skid Row once again. He would ask anyone who would talk to him if they'd seen anyone fitting Dani's description. Per usual, no one had anything to say. Not even when he gave them money. They were either a loyal group, or they didn't trust anyone enough to speak to them.

Claire silently thanked her dad. This was going to be hard enough to say without her mom being upset with her.

"Guys, I've been struggling with how to say this. I know you've been worried about her just as much as I have. But this isn't easy, so I need you to be patient with me, okay?" Claire's parents eyed each other and then nodded. "Thank you. As I was saying, I got this call not too long ago from a woman named Ellie Montgomery. When she said Dani wanted to see me, I was as stunned as you are."

"Who is this woman?" Karen asked. "A doctor?"

"No, she's a diner owner." Claire laughed softly. "Dani wouldn't talk to anyone, but her doctor asked Ellie to talk to her. Ellie brought Dani pie, and she opened up like they were BFFs."

Karen's lips twitched. "That sounds like our Dani. Go on."

"Okay, well . . ." Claire hesitated, looking for the right words. "I didn't know if I wanted to talk to Dani. It'd been two years, you know. I was mad. I *am* mad. But then, Ellie said that Dani had been in an accident, and I knew I couldn't stay away."

Jose leaned over and took his daughter's hand. He wasn't surprised when Karen did the same. "What kind of accident?" he asked quietly. Anything could happen out there on the streets. Especially to a sixteen-year-old girl. Most of those things ran through his head. Drug overdose, roughed up by a john, beaten by a gang. Each scenario made Jose's heart ache.

"She was hit by a car," Claire answered, her eyes filling with tears.

"Oh my God. Is Dani okay? How hurt is she?" Karen shook her head and apologized for interrupting. She had been so worried about all the other things that could hurt Dani out there. Karen never imagined it could be something like being hit by a car.

"She's alive, Mom, but I can't say she's okay. She has a broken arm, some broken ribs," Claire stopped and took another breath. "Her legs . . ."

"Son of a bitch!" Jose burst out of his seat before Claire

could even finish her sentence. "If that girl is paralyzed, I'll find Rita myself and make her pay!"

"Jose, please," Karen tried soothing. Though, she didn't blame him at all for his outburst. Dani *and* Claire had been through so much these past couple of years. Having one more hurtle like paralysis would be too much. *Fucking Rita.* "Is Dani paralyzed, Claire?"

It took Claire a moment for her mom's question to sink in. Would paralysis have been better for Dani? "No, she's not paralyzed," she said finally.

"Oh, thank goodness." Karen sat back in her chair with a sigh of relief.

"No, Mom. They're gone."

"What? Who's gone?" Jose asked. He was still trying to pace away his anger.

Karen, however, knew precisely what Claire meant. Claire could see it in her eyes. She could've kicked herself for the way she said it, but what's done is done. Now Claire had to put it all together for them.

"Her legs, Daddy."

"*Jesus,*" Karen murmured after the confirmation. Then the tears began.

It took Jose another second to catch up, and still, he couldn't wrap his brain around the news. "I don't understand." He frowned. "What do you mean they're gone?"

"Amputated, Daddy," Claire said softly. "Both of them."

Karen was openly weeping now. Jose sank back down into his chair, shaking his head. He was sure he had heard wrong. But when he saw his wife and daughter crying, he knew he hadn't.

"No. She's just a kid! Surely they could have done *something* different!" Jose wiped angrily at a tear. "She's just a kid," he said again with less energy. "The doctor who did this ..."

"Is devastated, Dad." Claire reached over and took his hand. "Dr. Vale, Hunter, has done so much to try and help Dani through this. I know it's hard to believe that any good could come out of this, but I'm trying so hard to see the good, guys. So hard."

"Dani's legs are gone, Claire Bear. What good is there in that?" Karen sniffled.

"Well, Dani happened to end up with an amazing, caring doctor who happened to know an equally amazing baker. It seems to have snowballed from there. Sometimes I can't believe it myself what they're doing for Dani."

"This Dr. Vale. Are we sure she's not trying to save her own ass? Did she botch something that caused Dani to lose her legs?"

"No, Daddy. And if you think I haven't thought of that, you obviously don't know how much of your daughter I am. But when you meet Hunter and Ellie, you'll see there is nothing malicious about them." Claire leaned her elbows on the table. "Hunter is even getting my apartment ready for Dani. You know, to be more accessible."

"There's no need for that," Jose stated. "You and Dani will come back here."

Wait, what? Claire did a mental double-take. "I have an apartment, Dad."

"Your dad is right, Claire. With all you do already, you won't be able to take care of Dani by yourself."

"I won't be by myself. I mean, we'll be alone at the apartment, but —" Claire sighed. "I didn't come here for you to dictate what's going to happen. Both Dani and I are adults. We still have so much to talk about and work out. But we can't do that here."

"Do you have any idea how to take care of a double amputee, Claire?" her father asked.

"Do *you*?" Claire countered. "I suspect it's going to be complete chaos until we find a rhythm. I would love it if you guys were around to help *when* we need it. But we can't move in here. We need our space. Besides, I'm pretty sure Dani is still scared of what you think about her."

Jose scoffed. "That's ridiculous. I've been looking for her ever since she took off."

"She didn't just take off, Dad."

He waved away her words. "You know what I mean." Jose scrubbed his face. "Where was she?"

"Skid Row," Claire answered honestly even though she knew what his reaction would be. She had waited to tell her parents partly out of fear, partly out of selfishness.

"I've been there! I searched for her! Goddammit, if I could have just found her!"

"It's not your fault, Dad." Claire pushed her plate away. The burger had looked and smelled good before this conversation. Now she couldn't bring herself to eat. "We haven't really talked about what went on out there yet. Dani is dealing with so much. But we'll have to get through it eventually to heal. And I don't think we can do that here. I know you're going to worry, but you're just going to have to trust us."

Jose shook his head. "I don't like it. You've taken on too much already. That apartment of yours isn't suitable for someone in a wheelchair." His voice cracked, but he cleared his throat and went on. "Dani needs someone to take care of her now. And while I know you're capable, Claire Bear, I don't want you to get overwhelmed with all this. Karen?"

Karen wiped her tears away and sat up straight. "Claire is an adult, Jose." She gave her husband a look when he began to argue. "Let's treat her like an adult. Now, you say this doctor is helping you with the apartment, right?" Claire nodded. "So, that's covered. What happens when the bills start coming in? The surgery, the hospital stay? I'm sure Dani will need to do physical therapy. I'm guessing she doesn't have insurance. Are you supposed to pay for that, Claire? I know you love her, but you're already spreading yourself thin. You make enough for your rent and food. How do you plan to deal with everything that's coming?"

Claire squared her shoulders and captured her mother's gaze. She knew what Karen was doing. And while she didn't like it, Claire understood.

"Well, Mom, Hunter waived her fee for the surgery. This is what I was talking about when I said there were good things to come out of this. One is the people we've met. They've advocated for Dani. Apparently, they're *very* connected as well. Dani's bills have been paid. That includes any future medical and physical therapy bills. She's even getting prosthetics. Good ones, too. All paid for. So, all I really need from you guys is your support. And maybe some emotional support when I need it. And perhaps you could come by and show Dani that you don't hate her because we're together?"

Karen and Jose were speechless. The young girl that thought the streets were better than accepting help was accepting help. They weren't sure if they should be pissed or happy that Dani had learned a lesson. And then there were these people, strangers that were helping Dani and Claire. What did they want in return? No one did things like this out of the goodness of their hearts. Did they?

"Of course, you have our support. And anything else you need," Karen began. "But I have to ask, why would these strangers do all this for you and Dani? You don't find it a bit strange?"

Claire chuckled. "I did until I spent more time with them. When I said Hunter was devastated by having to take Dani's legs, I wasn't exaggerating. She checks on Dani all the time. I still see the sorrow in her eyes. Look, I don't know what made them choose to help Dani. Maybe because they're lesbians, too? They know Dani's story. They know about Rita. Maybe they just wanted to give Dani a chance at the life she deserved."

"I want to meet them," Jose demanded. "And I want you checking in every week. Maybe you should give up this internship . . ."

"No," Karen interrupted. She shot her husband a disapproving look. "You don't give up anything, young lady. That internship is something you've wanted for a long time, and you worked hard to get it. We could help with bills if you need to cut back on your hours at work. And we'll be there whenever you need us."

"Every goddamn day," Jose muttered, cursing Rita with every fiber of his being.

"Not every day, Daddy. Please," Claire laughed. "But I would like you there this weekend. Dani is finally getting out of the hospital. I'd like for you to come to see her after she's settled in."

"We could help . . ."

"No, Mom. Dani is having a hard time accepting everything already. I think she just needs some time to adjust before she sees you two. I thought it was best if it was just her and me the first couple of nights."

"I suppose you're right. But you'll let us come visit soon?" Karen asked expectantly. She could've throttled her daughter for not informing them sooner of Dani's condition. But she had to respect that decision.

"Yes, of course. As I said, this weekend should be good. I'll run it by Dani, but I think she'll want to see for herself that you two still love her."

"And these women helping you both?" Jose prompted.

Claire rolled her eyes. "I will set up a time for you to meet." Claire perked up. "Maybe we could go to Ellie's Diner! That's perfect! I'll talk to Ellie about it and let you know when."

Chapter Sixteen

"You ready to be sprung?"

Dani looked over and saw Hunter standing at the door with a wheelchair. *Fucking wheelchair.* She shrugged sullenly. "Guess so."

"I thought you'd be happy to get out of here."

"I am." Dani scratched her head with her good hand. "You're still, like, my doctor, right?"

"Yes." Hunter rolled the wheelchair inside and locked the wheels.

"So, there's still the privacy thing?"

"Doctor-patient confidentiality. Yes," Hunter assured. "You're doing great, by the way."

Dani was sitting up on her bed, something she had been practicing for the past couple of weeks. Hunter was impressed with Dani's ability to adapt. The hospital's physical therapist had been by many times to get Dani ready for what was to come. It was going to be a hard road for the young woman. But Hunter was determined to be there every step of the way as long as Dani would let her.

"Thanks. It's weird, ya know? Sometimes it feels like they're still there. Other times, I just feel pain on the stumps."

Hunter came around the wheelchair and sat down. "May I take a look?"

Dani shrugged and helped Hunter lift the long shorts she had on. "That's not really what I wanted to talk to you about," she confessed.

Hunter looked up at Dani and smiled. "Okay. Well, I can do this and listen. I want to make sure everything is all right."

"You do that, like, every time you're in here," Dani laughed. "It's like you have OCD or something."

Hunter's smile faded. "I don't want anything else to happen to you, Dani. I'm so sorry."

"Nah, hey." Dani touched Hunter's shoulder since she was hunched over examining Dani's stump. "I understand now. I know I was pissed there for a while, but I think I was more scared than anything. I shouldn't have taken it out on you."

Hunter didn't want either one of them to dwell on that, so she changed the subject. "What is it you wanted to talk about?" she asked as she repositioned Dani's shorts legs back down.

"Right." Dani fidgeted so much she nearly fell over. "Damn it. Okay, is there, um," she huffed. "Is there any physical reason keeping me from, uh, you know . . ." Dani waved her arms around, hoping it would help Hunter understand what she was asking. All it did was cause her to lose her balance again.

Hunter sat back in the wheelchair and crossed an ankle over her knee. If she seemed relaxed — which she was far from at the moment — perhaps it would help Dani relax. She was a doctor. This should be easy for her. But if she correctly understood what Dani was asking, Hunter felt like she was having "the talk" with her kid.

"I'm assuming we're talking about you being intimate with Claire?" Hunter asked.

Dani blushed from torso to hairline. She was sure if she still had legs, they'd be blushing, too. "Yeah," she squeaked.

Hunter smiled kindly. "The answer is no. There's no

physical reason you can't be with Claire." She watched as the blush disappeared, and Dani turned pale. Hunter dropped her foot and leaned forward again. "However, there could be an emotional or mental setback, which is completely normal. Dani, no one expects you to be okay after everything you've been through."

But what if Claire expects it to be like it was before, Dani wondered silently. "How could she possibly be attracted to this?"

The far off look on Dani's face had Hunter wondering if Dani knew she asked the question out loud. "You know, I don't think it's any secret that Ellie and I are, um, involved."

Dani laughed despite her inner turmoil. "Not when you act like an idiot around her."

"Thanks for that," Hunter grumbled playfully.

"Just keepin' it real, doc," Dani shrugged.

Hunter rolled her eyes. "*Anyway.* I felt the way you did not too long ago. That someone like Ellie couldn't possibly be attracted to me."

"Are you kidding? Do you own a freakin' mirror?"

"Not everything we consider our flaws are visible, Dani. I've done things in my life I'm ashamed of. I was afraid when Ellie found out she wouldn't want to be with me."

"You could just not tell her, though. I can't hide this shit," Dani argued.

"You don't hide things from the ones you love. Ellie taught me that." Hunter sat back. "She also taught me that when you *are* loved," she gestured at herself and then at Dani's legs. "The outside is not what matters. But, Dani, you have to keep the communication open with Claire. Tell her how you feel. Tell her about your fears. I guarantee she has her own."

"Ellie teach you that, too? I swear that woman could convince anyone to tell her their deepest and darkest secrets," Dani mumbled.

Hunter laughed heartily. "I believe you're right. But she may be on to something. I still have regrets about the things I've done, but they don't consume me anymore. Having someone to love who loves you in return means you don't have to carry these burdens by yourself anymore, Dani. You just have to let them in."

Dani thought about what Hunter said for a long moment. "That easy?" she asked finally.

"Nope. But nothing worth anything in this world is easy. You just have to give it your best."

"Yeah." Dani tapped her blunt nails on the cast on her arm. "I wish I had my stuff, ya know. I wrote to Claire while I was out there. If she could read those, it may be easier for her to understand. I'm not that great at talking."

Hunter frowned. "Did they not give you your things?" She stood and walked to the little storage area in the room. She knelt and opened one of the drawers. "I told the nurse to make sure you knew this was here."

Hunter grunted as she pulled out Dani's duffel bag. *Iris*, she thought with a scowl. She had half a mind to have Iris fired. The young nurse's increasing incompetence and unwanted advances towards Hunter — despite Hunter's momentary stupidity — were getting problematic.

"Whoa! How'd?" Dani immediately started digging into the

bag when Hunter tossed it on the bed. She didn't have much, but it all seemed to be here. "How'd you get this?"

Hunter lifted a shoulder. "I, uh, found it when I went searching for who you were."

"Did — did you talk to anyone?" *Was it Angel? Was she mad?*

"I —" Hunter remembered Angel's warning. "I wasn't supposed to tell you how I got information about you. But lying to each other at this point isn't going to help anything. Which, by the way, I know how long you were really out there. Ellie does now, too." Hunter caught the shameful look on Dani's face and decided to move on. "I did talk to someone. A woman in a hoodie with a raspy voice."

"Angel," Dani said softly. "Was she pissed at me?"

"Pissed?" Hunter sat back down in the wheelchair. She found that when she didn't make it a big deal being in one in front of her patients, they had an easier time getting in it. "No, she seemed concerned. Why would she be mad at you?"

"I betrayed her," Dani confessed quietly. "She, like, takes care of people around there. Only asks for one thing in return. To stay out of trouble. I fucked up."

Hunter sighed. "First of all, don't let Ellie hear you talk like that. Second, whatever you did, this Angel person isn't holding it against you, Dani. She wants more for you. In fact, I had to promise you'd never end up back there, and I intend to keep that promise."

The door burst open before Dani could respond. Blaise Steele, as fiery as her name suggested, came charging in with her daughter Piper. Ellie and her daughter followed close behind.

Dani had met everyone earlier in her hospital stay. She had needed to know who was footing the bills. Needed to thank them. So, Ellie introduced them. Dani liked Blaise. The woman was a hoot to listen to with her New Zealand accent and no-nonsense attitude.

Then she met Piper and Jessie. To say it was shocking to find out Ellie had a daughter was an understatement. But Dani was pleased to find out that mother and daughter were very much alike. Piper, on the other hand, was the total opposite of her mother. Claire and Dani found an instant kinship with them both. Friendships weren't easy for Dani, but the four girls together — as different as they were — just . . . fit.

"Hello? Is this moving day, or what? Let's get a move on. I'm double parked."

"You are not double-parked, weirdo," Ellie laughed.

"No, but I've always wanted to say that." Blaise reached over and gave Dani a fist bump and a smile.

Ellie shook her head at her best friend. Then she walked past Hunter, giving her a cute wink, and hugged Dani. "Are you ready?"

"I think so. Where's Claire?"

"She had a few things to take care of, but she's on her way. We just wanted to stop by to see you before you got out of here."

"We're still going to see each other, right?" Dani asked. The trepidation in her voice was unmistakable.

"Uh, yeah, you are!" Jessie piped up. "I'm afraid you've got us for life, sis."

"It really is too late. Mum's jokes are all you can look forward to now," Piper quipped with a big grin.

"Keep it up, girlie, and I'll hide your baby brother's dirty nappies somewhere in your room."

Dani snickered. *"Nappies,"* she muttered cheerfully. She loved listening to Blaise and Piper. Not only because of their accents but because Dani got to learn new words for things.

"You want me to bring you some dirty nappies, Dani?" Blaise asked with a raised brow.

"No, thank you!" Dani cleared her throat. "Um, could I speak to you alone, Mrs. Steele?"

"Ugh! Only if you never call me Mrs. Steele again. That's my husband's mother and . . ." Blaise shivered dramatically. "Just, no."

Ellie laughed at her best friend, then turned to the others. "Come on. Let's give them a minute."

Blaise waited until the door was closed before she took a seat next to Dani on the bed. "What's up?"

"I, uh, just wanted to thank you for everything you're doing for me. I should have said that before, but . . . no buts. I should have said this earlier. Thank you."

Blaise smiled. "It's my pleasure."

"Why?" If Dani had legs, she would've kicked herself for asking the question. It was rude. To her relief, Blaise smiled. "I just don't know why you, Ellie, and the others are being so good to me."

"How much has Ellie told you about me, Dani?"

"Uh," Dani picked at the cast on her arm. "That you're her best friend, you love red velvet cake, and you were there for her when she needed you the most."

Blaise swallowed the lump in her throat. "So, just the important things," she said flippantly to keep the mood light.

"Here are the cliff notes, kid, because we don't have much time. Life for me before I became this incredible woman standing before you consisted of murder, kidnapping, and lies."

Dani's eyes widened as big as saucers. "Where can I read the full story, cuz that's blowing my fuckin' mind."

Blaise chuckled. "Don't let Ellie hear you talk like that. Maybe one day I'll tell you the full story. The moral of the story, however, is don't judge a book by its cover. You may think we have nothing in common, Dani, but we do even if the circumstances are different. My parents died when I was a little younger than you. Ellie's parents kept her from being who she is. We've all had times in our lives when we've needed someone's help. Now we have the means to pay it forward. You remind us of ourselves when we were your age. Do yourself a favor, accept the help, remember it, and pay it forward when you can."

"What if I disappoint you?"

"How would you do that?"

"I dunno," Dani shrugged. "Like, if I take too long in physical therapy or something."

Blaise laid a hand on what was left of Dani's leg. "You're not on a schedule, Dani. However long your recovery takes is how long it takes. Don't worry about anything except getting stronger." She leaned over and lowered her voice to a conspiratorial whisper. "I didn't mention in the cliff notes that I'm an heiress, did I?"

"Man! I *need* this book! Ooo! Maybe Claire could get that writer chick she loves so much to write your story."

Blaise laughed. "I'd much rather have a movie made. Maybe Angelina Jolie could play me," she winked. When her phone dinged, she checked the display. "It's Ellie. Claire is on her way up."

Dani took a deep breath. "Back to reality."

"At least this time you're with the person you love with a roof over your head."

Chapter Seventeen

The elevator ride up to Claire's apartment was just as quiet as the car ride. Neither Claire nor Dani knew what to say, and small talk seemed stupid. Dani found it weird that she could talk to someone like Blaise Steele just moments before Claire got to her room, then be all tongue-tied when Claire came in asking if she was ready.

"This is it," Claire said quietly when the elevator doors opened. She pushed the wheelchair out into the hallway and down towards her apartment.

At the hospital, Hunter had instructed Claire on how to get Dani in and out of the car. She showed her where to position the wheelchair, where to stand, and how to lift Dani without hurting herself. Days before Dani was released, both girls were instructed on bathroom and shower needs. Claire was feeling overwhelmed. Dani was feeling like a burden. Both wondered if this was going to work.

Claire stopped in front of a door and searched for her keys. "It's not much," she said absently as she unlocked the door.

"I've been living in a tent for two years, Claire," Dani responded without emotion.

Shit. "I, um, I'm sorry." Claire ran a hand through her hair. "I don't know what I can and can't say, Dani."

"You can say anything you want." Dani grabbed Claire's hand. "I don't want you to, uh, what do they say? Break eggshells?"

"Walk on eggshells," Claire offered.

"Right. I don't want that. I want you to be you."

Claire nodded and pushed the door open. "Ready?"

Dani shook her head. "Give me a minute."

"What's wrong?"

"I go in there, and everything is real, Claire. It's you and me. No nurses. No doctors." Dani looked up at Claire. "Are you sure about this?"

Claire tilted her head. "Are you thinking of running again?"

Dani looked down at where her legs should be. "I can't run anymore. If I wanted to leave, you'd have to push my ass." She looked back at Claire. "I'm asking *you* if you want to run, Claire. You didn't sign up for this shit."

"You're right, Dani, I didn't. But here we are."

"You think if I hadn't run away, this would never have happened, right?"

Claire knelt beside Dani's chair. "If is such a tiny word that carries such heavy burdens. If Rita hadn't been a bitch. If you hadn't run. If I had gone after you. If Dad had found you when he went out looking for you every night. *If. If. If.* We can't think about if now, Dani. We have to think about here and now."

"Heavy burdens," Dani repeated. "That was, like, some profound shit, Claire."

Claire burst out laughing. "Well, if I ever meet Joslyn Cohan, I'll tell her you think so. I read it in her book."

"Damn. Here I thought you were getting all smart and philosophical!"

Claire knew what Dani was doing, and she was grateful for it. Dani was never great with emotional talks. And Claire wasn't up for one right now, either. So, Dani's comedic interlude was just what they needed.

"I'll always be smarter than you, C-average," Claire teased.

"Whatever, nerd." Dani glanced inside the apartment. God, was she ready for Claire to see her at her most vulnerable? What alternative did Dani have? "Are we gonna go in, or do I have to sleep out here?"

Claire raised a brow. "Now that you brought it up, maybe sleeping out here would be a good punishment for you for being so ornery."

Dani shrugged a shoulder. "Okay. Just pop me a tent up." She grinned and winked at her girlfriend. Was that what Claire was again? Her girlfriend? And how long would that last when Claire had to wipe Dani's ass or wash her nether regions?

Claire rolled her eyes and pushed Dani into the apartment. "So, here's the kitchen," she announced, turning Dani towards the small galley kitchen. It was well appointed but too small for Dani's wheelchair. "When you get your legs, this will be easier for you to navigate. Maybe we should look for a bigger place? Mom and dad would help with rent if I . . ."

"Claire." Dani waited for Claire's slightly wild eyes to focus on her. "This place is great. I know things will be tough in the beginning, but we can do this. Right?"

Claire's eyebrows raised. "Look at you being all adult."

Dani snickered. "That sorta happens when you spend two years on the street."

"What else happens?" Claire asked softly. She didn't want to push Dani into talking about her time being homeless. But Claire knew it was a conversation that needed to happen. For Dani's sake more than Claire's.

Dani frowned. "Um."

"It's okay. Let's finish the tour of the apartment. I mean, it's grand, you know. It may take all night."

Dani thought about making another joke about her tent but decided against it. Claire was letting her off the hook and being cute and funny. "C'mon then. Get pushin', woman!"

Claire pushed Dani two steps forward. "Here's the living room slash dining room. And the first door on the right is the bathroom. The other door is the bedroom. Tour is done."

Dani laughed. "How about you actually take me to the other rooms so I can see how I'm going to do this."

"Right." Claire turned Dani towards the bathroom. "Hunter and Ellie persuaded the building owner to let them remodel some stuff to make it easier for you. I don't know how they convinced them, but here you go."

"She probably fed them her crack pies," Dani muttered as she took in the bathroom. The shower was definitely large enough to fit a wheelchair plus another person. She took a moment to think about what it would be like showering with Claire. The image used to excite Dani. Since it now filled her with trepidation, she focused on the sink. "Can you wheel me over there?"

Claire complied. She, too, had been thinking about the shower situation. With considerable will power, Claire tamped down the panic that threatened to boil over. She wanted to help Dani before. She wanted to help her now. It was time to suck it up and do everything she could do.

"This is nice," Dani said, reaching out to touch the sink. There was no cabinet underneath, so her wheelchair fit perfectly. "Is it too short for you?"

Claire chuckled. "Have you seen me? This may be too tall!"

Dani looked up and laughed. "Do you think when I get my legs, they'll give me ones that make me taller?"

"Nope. I'm going to make sure they keep you close to your height," Claire vowed.

"Why?"

"Uh, because I don't want to have to deal with more renovation in this bathroom! That sink is staying exactly where it is."

Dani snorted. "Fine. Are we sure my new wheelchair will fit?"

When Blaise learned that Dani was going home with a standard wheelchair, she was having none of it. Dani's arm would be in a cast for at least another month. Blaise made it clear that Claire couldn't be Dani's "chauffeur" twenty-four-seven, and a motorized wheelchair was in order. Dani's first instinct was to argue. Then she thought of the burden she would be on Claire and acquiesced. The new wheelchair was due to arrive the next day.

"I don't see why not. Hunter said they put it at the top of the required height because you'd be getting prosthetics. I think it'll be good."

Dani nodded and looked over at the toilet. There were grab bars on each side, not that Dani could use them now. But when her arm was healed, it would be helpful. The toilet also looked a bit taller than she was used to. Kinda like the one at the hospital. Since that seemed to help Claire when Hunter was going over this part with them, Dani was grateful. Hunter and Ellie really did think of everything. There was even a small cabinet close by where Dani was sure held all the necessary products girls needed.

"They installed a bidet," Claire told Dani. "Hunter said something about how a bidet would help with privacy. You know, um, you wouldn't have to rely on me if you needed solitude or something." She rolled Dani closer. "I mean, obviously, I'm going to have to help you get situated until your arm heals. But —"

"So, like, the bidet takes the place of toilet paper?" Dani leaned forward to look inside the toilet. "That looks, uh, scary."

Claire giggled. "It's actually quite refreshing."

Dani stared up at Claire. "You've used this thing?"

"Of course! I had to make sure it worked for you. I think you'll enjoy it." Claire winked. "The bathroom is accessible from the living room and the bedroom. Kinda like a Jack and Jill, you know? Ready to see the bedroom?"

Dani grabbed the wheel of her wheelchair before Claire could move her. "Hang on."

"Do you have to use the restroom?"

"N—no. I mean, not right now. We should talk about sleeping arrangements."

"Oh. Sorry. I guess I just assumed you'd be . . . Um, let's go out into the living room." Claire tapped Dani's hand and pushed her — maybe a little too fast — out of the bathroom.

"I didn't mean to offend you," Dani said quietly.

"You didn't. I shouldn't have assumed."

"Claire." Dani sighed. *Here goes nothing. I hope Hunter is right about this honesty shit.* "I'm scared."

Claire positioned Dani and then sat down on the couch, facing her. "Scared of what?"

"What you're going to think."

"Of?"

"This!" Dani said, slapping her leg. "Ouch. Remind me not to do that again."

Claire's brows furrowed. "I don't understand, Dani."

"I have no legs, Claire!"

"Yes, I've been aware of that for a few weeks now. That's why I don't understand. Did you think I'd forgotten?"

"No. But you didn't have to, like, see them. Or, you know, be near them. The stumps, I mean. It's not pretty. Hunter says I have another few weeks before everything heals completely."

Claire sat back. "That's what you're afraid of? That I'll think your wounds are *ugly*?"

"When you put it that way, it sounds . . ."

"Superficial?" Claire offered sarcastically.

"Are you gonna get mad at me every time I tell you my fears?" Dani asked seriously. Hunter hadn't told her about this part. She had made it seem all fine and dandy. Tell the truth, and there'd be no problems.

Claire closed her eyes and took a deep breath. "I'm sorry," she said finally. When she opened her eyes, Dani was staring at her. "I should have listened to your concerns without getting upset." *Even if you basically called me shallow.* Claire silently chastised herself for that thought. Dani wasn't trying to insult her. She was just trying to be honest. "I'm sorry," she repeated.

"S'okay. I guess we're gonna do this sometimes, huh?"

"I'll do my best not to be argumentative."

Dani scoffed. "You wouldn't be Claire if you didn't say your piece. I want you to be honest with me, too. Just maybe don't bite my head off? I can't afford to lose more body parts."

Claire hid her face in her hands and groaned. "You're going to keep making jokes, aren't you?"

"Better than being depressed, isn't it?"

With a peek through her fingers, Claire nodded. She scrubbed her face once, then sat up. "Okay, we came over here to talk about sleeping arrangements. I would like you to be in the bedroom with me. I'm sure we'll both have to adjust to all the changes. And we still need to have a long talk about everything. I'm not suggesting sex or anything. I'm suggesting that we do what we've done many times before when we were best friends. Sleep in the same bed."

All of Claire's words went through Dani's brain. Of course, being the asshole it was, her brain picked and chose which words to actually listen to. *Were. Sex.*

Dani glanced at Claire when she said her name. "What are we?" she asked roughly.

"What?"

"What are we? You said when we *were* best friends. That means you don't think we are anymore. You want to share a room but feel nothing sexual for me. I guess I'm confused." Dani winced inwardly, waiting for Claire to explode.

"I don't know," Claire answered softly. She stood up and began to pace. "We were best friends for so long. We knew everything about each other. Well," she gave Dani a small grin. "Almost everything. And then, for a few weeks, we had it all, Dani. The friendship, love, sex . . . a future."

"Then I ruined everything."

"Rita ruined it!" Claire groused. "My point is, it's been two years, and it feels more like a lifetime. We've both changed, Dani. We're going to have to get to know each other again. But that doesn't mean I don't love you. And I never said I feel nothing sexual. I'm just saying it's going to take a minute to find our way back to who we were. Or who we are now together."

"I should have stayed with you, Claire." Dani wiped a tear from her cheek. "I did everything wrong that day. That's why I don't get it."

"Get what?"

Dani couldn't stifle the yawn that came out of nowhere. As much as she tried to ignore the pain she was in, it continued to take a lot out of her.

"Sorry," Dani mumbled.

"How about we talk more later?" Claire suggested. "It's been a long day for you."

Dani raised a brow. "A long day? I was literally transferred from a bed to a wheelchair. Then *you* pushed me everywhere. It's only like . . . what time is it?"

Claire checked the time on the microwave. "Nine o'clock. And may I remind you that your body is healing," she grabbed the handles of Dani's wheelchair. "Plus, you have a big day tomorrow. Now, if you're not comfortable sleeping with me, I can sleep out here."

Tomorrow was Dani's first *official* day at physical therapy. She'd also be getting fitted for her prosthetics. *Don't forget the new wheelchair*, Dani thought, and shook her head. All the *help* was making her feel itchy. Or was that unworthy? Even after Blaise's explanation, Dani still didn't get it. But she would do what Blaise said and accept it. One day, when she could, she'd pay it forward.

"I can't let you give up your bed. So, like, we don't know where we stand, but I'd like to sleep in the bedroom with you,"

Dani said as Claire wheeled her to the bathroom. "Except, uh, I don't have any clothes."

"There's nothing in the bag you had with you?" Claire rolled her eyes. "Which we apparently left in the car." She'd been so focused on getting Dani out of the car without hurting her that she forgot to pick up Dani's bag.

"Nah. Well, nothing that's been washed in the past few weeks."

"Okay. Well, I think I have some sweats here. Maybe a few t-shirts. We'll have to go shopping for some essentials tomorrow when I get off work. Until then, I'll run down to the car to get your bag and do a load of laundry before I go to bed. You'll need some underwear for tomorrow." Claire mentally checked her schedule. She could blow off the two classes she had tomorrow. That wasn't anything she couldn't make up or ask for notes on. Her internship was a bit trickier.

"Hey, Claire?" Dani knew that look from before. Claire would zone out when she was trying to solve problems. She was pretty damned good at it, but if Dani didn't get Claire's attention now, they could be there for hours.

Claire blinked. "Yeah?"

"I don't think I'll fit in your stuff. You're kinda tinier than I am."

Crap. "It's, uh, not mine," Claire stammered. She hadn't told Dani about Cris. She was kind of hoping she would never have to.

"Oh." The look on Claire's face told Dani everything she needed to know. Well, it told her things she didn't want to know, especially right now when Claire was about to help her get ready for bed. "Okay."

That's it? No questions? What did that mean? Did Dani not care what Claire had been up to? She had to admit that neither of them talked about anything important during their time apart. Mostly, Claire watched Dani sleep. Or she paid attention to the physical therapist that would come into the room and work with Dani. Or Claire would listen to Hunter discuss medications and expectations. Then, of course, there was Ellie and her food, and Blaise and her charitable self. A couple of weeks ago, Jessie and Piper showed up on the scene, and they all became fast friends who talked about many things . . . and nothing at all. It occurred to Claire now that she and Dani were very content to let the others do the talking.

"Um, do you want to take a shower?" Claire asked, her voice a tad insecure.

"Nah. Unless I smell." Dani raised the arm without the cast and sniffed herself. "I think I'm okay. A shower would mean changing all the dressings and stuff, and that's a headache."

"All right. Do you need to go to the bathroom?"

"Uh, yeah, I kinda do."

Claire sensed Dani's uneasiness. "You just want to use the bidet, don't you?" she teased.

"Caught me," Dani laughed, relieved. "How are we, like, supposed to do this? You had a rough time getting me in and out of the car, and that was just, like, scooching me. I can't take a shower in a wheelchair. Especially the motorized one I'm getting. And I don't think 'scooching' is going to work for the toilet."

"Ah-ha!" Claire exclaimed. "We got sidetracked, and I didn't get to show you the cool contraption Hunter brought in. Wait here."

Dani chuckled. "Yeah, okay." She watched Claire hurry out the door that led to her bedroom. *Their* bedroom. Claire may not know what label to put on their relationship, but to Dani, Claire would always be *the one*. She didn't need a ton of talking or time to figure that part out. But she would give Claire all the time she needed. The talking would be harder, but Dani would figure it out.

"Back!"

"What the hell is that?" Dani stared at the contraption Claire pushed into the bathroom. It looked like one of those baby swings only bigger. *This is my life now*, Dani thought miserably.

"It's a sling." *A toilet sling*, Claire corrected silently. By the look on Dani's face, she was already having a hard time with this contraption. "Basically, we get this thing under you," Claire showed Dani the blue mesh sling that had four clips and a hole in the middle. "Then, when you need to go to the bathroom or take a shower, we hook the clips here, here, here, and here, push the button, and voila!"

Dani knew Claire was doing her best to make everything out to be a good thing. A fun thing. But all Dani could think was how freakin' helpless she was. She tried shaking off the depression.

"That thing goes in the shower?" Dani asked skeptically.

"Well, no. I mean, there's another chair in there that we'd transfer you to. This thing, as you call it, just helps me move you where you need to go."

"So, I can't do it by myself?"

Claire shook her head. "No, I'm sorry. But I'll do whatever you need me to do to make this easier on you." She held up a finger, then hurried out of the room again. When she came back in, she was carrying a blanket. "I figured we could use this to cover you when you have to go to the bathroom. I don't know how to give you more privacy when taking a shower, though."

Dani shrugged as nonchalantly as she could. "It's not like you haven't seen me naked before."

Claire's skin turned hot as she blushed. "I know, but . . ."

"Claire, thank you. You didn't have to put yourself through all this shit. Especially after what I did to you. I don't deserve your forgiveness, let alone your help."

Claire knelt next to Dani. "There were many things you didn't deserve. Your mom kicking you out of the house, being out on the streets, being hit by a car, losing your legs. My forgiveness? My help? That's easy for me, Dani." She scoffed. "Well, not easy. But easier than knowing you're out there somewhere alone, but not knowing where."

Dani took Claire's hand that was resting on her stump. When Claire jumped slightly, Dani knew Claire didn't even realize she had put it there.

"The blanket is a good idea," she said softly, stroking the back of Claire's hand with her thumb. "I know we've been, uh, intimate before. But using the toilet in front of you is a whole other weird thing."

Claire chuckled. "I agree."

"As for the shower, I'll probably need your help until this thing comes off." Dani held up her casted arm. "It's up to you how you want to handle that. I mean, I have to be naked, but you don't." She blushed furiously as she said the words.

"We'll work it out. Besides, once you get your legs and the use of your arm back, you'll be able to do all that yourself, right?"

Dani's lips curved. "Yeah. Okay! So, what's the first step here with this thing? Cuz I really gotta pee."

Claire laughed and patted Dani's thigh. "Alright." She stood and grabbed the sling off the device. "We're going to situate this underneath you. Then I'll cover you up and help you out of your shorts and stuff."

"I guess that hole is there for a good reason," Dani said, eyeing the sling.

"Yep. Anyway, while you're going, I'll go and get you some clothes to sleep in."

"'Kay." What other choice did Dani have but to comply? She wouldn't be able to take care of herself for another few weeks. Dani wondered if she had it in her to rely on others for that long.

It took them a few minutes to get everything in place. Claire was clocked by Dani's casted arm more times than not. But that was the easy part. Now, Claire had to take Dani's clothes off. This was completely different than the other times she had done this. There was nothing sexual. And she was sure Dani was having as much of a problem with this as she was. She put the blanket over Dani's lap.

"Okay, so I'm going to tug your shorts and stuff down. You good with that?"

Dani nodded.

"I'll keep you covered. Then I'll lift you and get you settled. When you're done, push this button here for the bidet." Claire gave Dani a quick tutorial on how to use the fancy toilet. "I'll be right outside the door, so when you're finished, just call out. I'll come in and get you dressed for bed."

"Yeah, okay." Dani held her breath as Claire slipped her hand underneath the blanket. She had dreamt about being with

Claire again every night. *This* was not how those dreams went. There wasn't an ounce of arousal when she felt Claire unbutton her shorts or pull them down. There was only humiliation.

Claire tossed Dani's shorts and underwear to the side. "Are you okay?"

Dani shrugged.

"Alright, I'm going to hook you up and start lifting you. If *anything* hurts, let me know immediately." Claire began to hook the sling up the way Hunter showed her. She had practiced this over and over again before bringing Dani home. Being a nurse was not Claire's forte, but the last thing she wanted to do was hurt Dani any more than she already was. "Are you in any pain? Any discomfort?" Claire asked when she began the lift.

Dani shook her head. "No pain. Can't say there's no discomfort, though."

Claire stopped. "Is something pinching?"

"No, I just meant I'm embarrassed."

"I know, babe. But we've got this. Everything will be fine."

"Promise?"

Claire looked up at Dani. "I promise." She moved the lift over to the toilet and began the descent, making sure her positioning was right. "The sling should help you keep your balance. I'm going to step out and find those clothes, okay?"

"Yeah." Dani waited until the door closed behind Claire before she let the tears fall.

Chapter Eighteen

"Do you want to wear these?" Claire held up a pair of worn — but relatively intact — jeans. She had washed all the clothes in Dani's bag, saddened by how they looked now. She remembered when Dani had stuffed them in that damned duffel bag.

"Do you think I could stay in these?" Dani picked at the sweats she was wearing — doing her best to not think about whose they were. "I think I'll be doing some exercises and stuff."

"Sure." Claire's phone dinged, and she checked the incoming text. Her stomach dropped when she saw the name Anne Davis attached to it. "*Shit.*"

"Problem?"

"No. Yes." She sighed. "I just got a text from my boss at the publishing company. I have to go to the office for a *talk.*" Claire glanced at her backpack, which held the book she should've finished reading by now. Hell, she should have notes to turn in at this point. She had wanted to read some last night, but instead spent the night wide-eyed and afraid to move. Claire hadn't wanted to disturb Dani or accidentally hurt her. What she got in return was a stiff body, loss of sleep, and nowhere closer to finishing the book she desperately needed — and wanted — to finish.

"Oh. Well, I'm sure I could get Ellie or someone to pick me up if you can't."

Claire waved that away. "No, no. I'll just text Mom. She can pick you up."

"Wh-what?"

Claire tore her gaze away from her phone and looked at Dani's stricken face. "What, what?"

"W-why would she do that?" Dani's heartrate tripled at the news.

"Pick you up? Because my parents are coming over to see you. Mom can just stop by to get you before coming here," Claire answered as if it were the stupidest question ever spoken.

"But why? They never came to see me at the hospital. I thought they hated me."

Claire cursed again, this time because of her own stupidity. She should've had this conversation with Dani already. "They didn't know you were there, Dani." She walked into the living room and sat close to Dani. "I didn't tell them until yesterday. That's why I was late picking you up."

"Oh. Ellie told me you were running errands. I guess I assumed you were buying groceries or something. Why didn't you tell them before? Because they hate me?"

"Will you stop saying that! They don't hate you. I didn't tell them because . . . because I didn't know how. I also had to make sure that *this* would actually happen. They lost you once. I didn't want to do that to them again."

Dani frowned. "But you've known I'd be coming here for weeks." She paused when she saw the look on Claire's face. "Did you think I was lying?"

"Not lying. But, Dani, you fight so much when people want to help you. And now that you have tons of people who are willing, I was afraid you would get overwhelmed and . . ."

"Bolt again?" Dani guessed.

Claire shrugged. "My parents weren't exactly happy with me that I kept this from them for so long. But they agreed to let you get settled in last night before they bombarded you with hugs."

"So . . . they're not mad at me?"

"Do you think Dad would look for you almost every night for two years if they were?"

"Maybe," Dani said softly. "If he, ya know, came looking for me with a cop."

Claire looked up sharply. "You saw him?"

Dani nodded. "I hid. Before you start yelling at me, he was there with a cop! I thought they were there to arrest me! I'm sorry!"

Claire studied Dani. She tried to step into Dani's shoes and imagine how scary it would be to see a cop looking for her — especially with the father of the girl she was caught kissing. Dani hadn't known that Claire's parents had accepted Claire's sexuality. All Dani could remember is her mother disowning her.

"I get it," Claire said finally. "I wouldn't tell him you saw him, though. Let Dad live in contented bliss without knowing you avoided him." She stood up when Dani agreed. "Mom texted back, by the way. Are you okay with her picking you up?"

"Yeah." Dani leaned her head back and looked up at Claire when she started to push her wheelchair towards the front door. "Are you going to be okay? You know, at your work?"

Probably not. "I'm sure everything will be fine. Ready for this?"

Not really. "Let's do it!"

When Claire walked into the publishing office, she was shaking so bad her teeth were chattering. It had nothing to do with the weather and everything to do with nerves. This was it. She was done in this industry before she even began.

"She's waiting for you."

Claire nearly jumped out of her skin, hearing Anne's assistant's voice. "T-thanks, Sophie." She paused. "How much trouble am I in?"

Sophie's face scrunched up in sympathy. "Maybe we can still get coffee together?"

"Shit." Claire took a long, deep breath. Then knocked on Anne's door. "Ms. Davis?"

"Get in here, Oliver!"

Claire barely opened the door enough to slip inside. Once in, she stood there like a statue. Or like a dog that was about to be reprimanded and sent to the doghouse. Anne Davis was intimidating when she was smiling. When she frowned, it was downright scary.

Anne looked up and frowned. "I said get in here. Sit down."

"Yes, ma'am." Claire hurried to the guest chair and sat on the edge. "Ms. Davis . . ."

"Did you finish the book?"

"No, ma'am, but . . ."

"When you came to me begging for an internship, I was skeptical, Oliver. But you convinced me you could do this. I carved out a place for you, and you failed me! How do you think it makes me look to our clients when I don't have reliable people?"

Anne's booming voice caused Claire to shrink back in the chair. "I'm sorry, Ms. Davis. I've been . . ."

"Doing nothing!" Anne yelled. "That's what you've been doing. Did you come here from a competitor? Are you trying to destroy me? My company?"

"No, ma'am! If I could just . . ."

"What? Hmm? Make excuses? Blame others for your incompetence?"

Before Claire could respond, the door to Anne's office opened.

"Anne? What on earth is going on in here?"

Claire had never seen Anne Davis look chagrined before. It softened her whole face, making her look at least five years younger. Curious as to who could possibly have that effect on her hard-nosed boss, Claire turned to the visitor. Her eyes widened, and she jumped out of her chair, comically close to standing at attention. Joselyn Cohan.

"Jos, you're early."

"Yes, I know. You should be thankful for that since I'm usually late." Jos turned her gaze to the young woman in the room with them that Anne rudely forgot to introduce. She held out her hand. "Hello. I'm Joselyn Cohan."

Claire stared at the elegant hand for way too long before remembering her manners. She discreetly — she hoped — wiped her palm on her slacks before accepting the handshake. "I, um, know. You're my favorite author," she gushed.

Jos smiled. "Thank you so much. And your name?"

"Oh! Sorry, I'm Claire Oliver."

Jos's smile brightened. "My beta reader!"

"Former," Anne groused.

"Why is that?" Jos asked with a concerned frown.

"Because I haven't finished reading, Ms. Cohan," Claire confessed. "I was given a deadline, and I completely missed it."

Jos tilted her head and studied the girl. She looked incredibly young, but Jos knew the intelligence behind that youth. Claire Oliver was one of the most talented editors she had come across in her writing career. She knew that Claire wasn't technically an editor, but the girl was smart enough — thorough enough — to become one. A great one.

"Why? Are you not enjoying it?"

Claire's eyebrows shot up. "I am! Oh my god, it is so good!"

"Then, if I may ask, why the delay?"

Anne stood, trying to be imposing. But neither woman was paying any attention to her anymore. It was time for Anne to show them who ran the joint. "Jos, let me handle this, please."

Jos held up a hand towards Anne. "You handling it was yelling at her loud enough for everyone to hear. Did you ask her to explain? Did you ask if anything was wrong that would prevent her from doing a job you know she's excellent at?"

Anne frowned again. "No. I don't need excuses. I need people who can do the job. And so do you. You don't have time to be sitting around waiting for things to get done on time."

"I need Claire on my team, Anne. You've seen her notes. You've seen how meticulous she was with grammar and letting me know what worked and what didn't. Someone with that amount of attention to detail must have a reason for not getting something done on time."

Claire gulped when Jos turned her gaze back on her. *She's so pretty.* Joselyn Cohan was striking. She was the epitome of a beautiful California girl with her blonde hair, blue eyes, and slim figure. Add that together with high cheekbones, full lips, and almond-shaped eyes that squinted slightly with an ever-present smile. It equaled dreamy. This woman, Claire thought, should be on TV. It was also a face that made you want to tell every little secret you held inside you. And that's exactly what Claire did.

She told Jos everything. Starting from the beginning with when Claire learned she was in love with Dani — ending with how she was now Dani's primary caretaker. Claire even sprinkled in how she didn't know if she could trust Dani yet. And how she wasn't sure how to describe their relationship. She loved Dani with all her heart. Her heart, however, just wasn't fully repaired from being shattered into pieces. Once all was said and done, Claire had left nothing out. She also forgot that her boss was still in the room. *Shit.*

"Wow." Jos plopped down in one of the guest chairs, gesturing for Claire to sit, too. "That's quite a lot to deal with. For both of you."

"Yes," Claire agreed. "But it's not an excuse." She glanced at Anne.

Jos looked over at Anne as well. "You didn't know any of this?"

Anne shook her head. She agreed it was a lot. But she didn't think it was enough to let the girl off the hook for being late on her deadline. You didn't get ahead in this business by being a pushover.

"Claire is right. It doesn't excuse her lack . . ."

"Anne, stop," Jos sighed and focused on Claire again. "Okay. It seems like there are a lot of people helping Dani out. Which is great, don't get me wrong. But I'm worried about you."

"They're there to help me, too," Claire said quickly.

"I'm sure they'll do what they can. From what you've told me, it sounds like you're surrounded by great people. However, you're spreading yourself too thin, Claire."

"Please, Ms. Cohan, don't fire me! I love doing this, and I swear I'll do better!"

"First, call me Joslyn. Or Jos. Second, I don't want to fire you. I want to hire you."

"Huh?"

"What?" Anne squeaked. "Jos, we don't have the funds . . ."

"I didn't say *you* would hire her, Anne. I said I would." Jos leaned forward in her seat, looking Claire in the eye. "School, a job, and this internship. With being Dani's primary caretaker, you're going to burn out sooner rather than later. Would you like to hear my suggestions?"

"Yes, ma'am."

Jos chuckled. The girl was young enough that Joselyn could most likely be her mother. Still, she hated being called ma'am. "Your job keeps the rent paid, yes?" Claire nodded. "You're going to school to become an editor?"

"To begin with," Claire answered.

Jos smiled. "You want Anne's job, don't you? *That's* why she's so salty with you." Jos winked at the older woman sitting behind the desk, scowling. "Here's the deal. Work with me as my assistant. We'll work out a salary that is comparable to what you're making now so that you can keep paying rent and be comfortable. You would also quit interning here."

"Hey!" Anne interjected.

"What? You wanted to 'fire' her five seconds ago. Work with me here, Anne. You've been my publisher for years. I've made you a ton of money. I also know you could have afforded to pay Claire."

"She was getting paid in experience, Jos," Anne grumbled. She wanted to argue more, but Jos was right. Joselyn Cohan made Anne's publishing company what it was today. And Anne was driving an expensive car and living in a luxury apartment in Los Angeles.

"Experience doesn't pay the bills, Anne. Nor does it give her time to breathe when she's going through so much. None of that is your fault or your burden to fix," Jos reassured.

"Nor is it yours," Anne mumbled.

Jos's ever-present smile never wavered. "I'm not trying to fix everything. I'm merely trying to help. And I have selfish reasons for it. We can't all be altruistic, can we, Claire?" she winked.

"I, uh, I don't understand." Claire moved restlessly in her seat. Her leg bounced uncontrollably. What could Joselyn Cohan possibly want in return for helping? Was she about to be disappointed by her favorite author?

"Don't look so nervous! My selfish reason is to keep you as my beta reader. I wasn't exaggerating when I said I needed you on my team. Claire, your notes have saved me tons of time and given me many ideas on how to better my writing. How to be more open with my characters. Seeing them through your eyes has given me a different perspective. No other beta reader has done that for me. And no editor has been as thorough."

"Thank you." Claire lowered her eyes shyly. She strived to be the best at what she did. While accolades were great in the form of success, compliments made Claire uncomfortable. Perhaps Jos was right. Not everyone could be altruistic. Didn't Claire have selfish reasons? Selfish goals?

"It's the truth," Jos asserted. "And now my other selfish reason. Before I say this, know that your answer will not affect anything I've already offered. If you want the job, it's yours. I would like to talk to Dani about her experiences out on the streets."

Claire inhaled sharply. She hadn't expected that request. "Why?"

"Because sitting here talking to you, listening to you, has given me an idea for a book. It would be for research purposes only. And I could pay Dani for her time."

"She hasn't even talked to me about that," Claire confessed.

"Sometimes, it's easier to open up to a stranger. The good thing about that is, once the dam is broken, it gets easier to talk to loved ones."

Claire mulled over Jos's words. She had read all the Joselyn Cohan books, and one thing Claire knew for sure, Jos was diligent in her research. It was evident in the way she wrote. Jos must have spoken to tons of people about many different things. What if it could help Dani? Claire knew the prospect of getting paid would help Dani feel less like a burden.

"I can't guarantee she'll say yes," Claire finally answered.

Jos shrugged. "All I need is a guarantee you'll ask. The rest is up to Dani."

Claire pursed her lips. "Quit my job and the internship and come work for you?" She wanted to reiterate the deal in case her giddy fangirling self was making things up in her head.

"Yes."

"I have classes three times a week."

"Sounds reasonable."

"And you'll pay me what I'm making now?"

"Or more," Jos smiled. "We want you comfortable."

A grin slowly took place on Claire's face. She held her hand out enthusiastically. "Deal!"

Jos smiled brightly and shook Claire's hand. "Deal."

Anne frowned. "What the fuck just happened?"

Chapter Nineteen

Dani pressed the lever of her new wheelchair forward. Once she ran out of room to go any further, she pulled the lever back, rolling backward. She hit the wall behind her and started over.

"Are you pacing?" Blaise stuffed copies of the paperwork she just filled out into her briefcase.

"Maybe," Dani muttered, then remembered who she was talking to. "Um, thank you for this. And the legs."

"You already thanked me. I think we're up to thirty-five times now." Blaise stood in front of Dani's chair to stop her. "You don't have to thank me every time you see me. That would be awkward for us both."

"Sorry."

"I hear physical therapy went well. And the prosthetics shouldn't take too long."

"Yeah," Dani answered distractedly.

"Want to tell me what's wrong? You're considerably monosyllabic today. More so than usual."

Dani apologized again and sighed. "Claire's mom is picking me up. I haven't seen her since I, um, left. I'm nervous."

"Nervous or scared shitless?" Blaise teased.

"Let's go with shitless," Dani snickered. "Though, Claire has a great bidet for that."

Blaise smirked and raised a brow. "I love my bidet." She leaned a shoulder against the wall. "They didn't visit you in the hospital?"

"Long story," Dani said. Then changed her mind and told

Blaise how Claire hadn't trusted Dani enough to tell her parents until last night.

"Hmm. I suppose I can understand Claire's hesitation."

Dani glowered. Shouldn't someone be on her side with this?

"Don't you frown at me," Blaise scolded with levity. "It's the whole fool me once thing." When Dani stared at her with a blank look, Blaise explained further. "Fool me once, shame on you. Fool me twice, shame on me. Look, sweets, I'm not saying you'll run away again. I'm saying Claire has a legitimate fear of being hurt again."

"Yeah, I guess. But technically, I ain't running anywhere ever again."

Blaise rolled her eyes. "People do incredible things with prosthetics. Including running, kiddo." She put a hand on Dani's shoulder. "However, you can't keep running from your past. Eventually, it catches up to you."

"So, I should suck it up and face my fears?"

"Exactly," Blaise smiled. "Come on. I'll follow you outside and wait until she gets here."

"You don't have to do that."

"I know I don't. Come on."

Blaise took off down the hall, and Dani had no other choice but to follow. Dani was kinda glad Blaise would be with her when Claire's mother showed up. Maybe it would make things less awkward by letting the "grownups" talk. Then again, what would she talk to Blaise about as they waited? Dani was never good at small talk. Fortunately, Dani saw a very familiar SUV as soon as she and Blaise walked outside. Unfortunately, it was *not* Claire's mom. It was Jose.

"Oh, shit."

Blaise glanced down at Dani. "Problem?"

"That's Claire's dad."

"Ooo, the ol' parental switcharoo. I'm almost sad that I have to get back to the shop. This looks like it could be more entertaining."

Dani looked up at Blaise and saw her smiling. The woman was freakin' awesome. She never treated Dani like a former homeless — now handicapped — teenager. No, Blaise teased Dani like every other person in her life. As much as it frustrated Dani, she loved it.

"You, uh, don't want to meet him?"

"Sure I do." Blaise watched as a well-built man of average size got out of the SUV. He wasn't as opposing as she thought he would be by the look of fear in Dani's eyes. Then again, Blaise was used to the intimidating size of her husband. *I suppose this man could be scary to a teenager*, she thought.

"Dani!" Jose quickly found his way to the young woman, immediately falling to his knees in front of her. He wanted to cry when he saw what was left of her legs, but he held it in. Jose wanted to shout at her for not letting them help, but he held back. He wanted to hug her. She had been like another daughter to him for many years before they lost her. This time, he didn't stop himself. Jose wrapped his arms around Dani and held on tight. When he felt Dani's arm snake around him and hug him back, Jose allowed a couple of tears of joy free.

Blaise watched the scene with fascination. Claire's father wasn't at all frightening. Even as he gave Dani a fierce hug, Blaise noticed how he took care not to hurt Dani. She wondered what Dani's life would have been if Dani had allowed the Olivers to help her. Perhaps they wouldn't be where they were now. She shook her head slightly. Ego could really be a bitch.

"I'm sorry, I don't mean to interrupt this reunion," Blaise said awkwardly. She had contemplated leaving but thought that would have been ruder than interrupting.

"Oh, sorry." Jose chuckled nervously as he stood up. "I'm Jose Oliver. Are you a nurse here?"

Blaise looked down at her tailored clothes and chuckled. "I wish I had the capacity to be a nurse," she confessed. "Nevertheless, I'm merely a flower shop owner." She shook Jose's hand. "Blaise Steele."

"Uh, Blaise is my, um . . ." Dani stammered, trying to find the right words. How the hell did one explain how someone they practically just met was now paying for a bunch of shit for you?

"Friend," Blaise offered. "And benefactor, I suppose."

"Ah, you're the one helping Dani with everything." Jose shook Blaise's hand even more enthusiastically. "I don't know how to thank you!"

"Please don't," Blaise laughed.

"Yeah, she's tired of that. I think I'm banned from ever saying it again."

"Ah, well." Jose shuffled his feet a bit, not knowing what to say if he couldn't thank this woman for everything she was doing. "Um, if there's ever anything you need, please don't hesitate to ask. I'm a lawyer — a damn good one if I may say so myself."

Blaise smiled. "I hope I never need your services, Mr. Oliver."

"Jose, please."

"Jose. I have to get back to the shop. It was nice meeting

you," she said to Jose. "And, you," Blaise looked at Dani. "Be good."

"Do I gotta?" Dani whined with a grin.

"I'm afraid so." Blaise glanced back at Jose's SUV. "This contraption she's in now folds up. You shouldn't have any problems fitting it in your car, but I'm not sure about Claire's."

Jose nodded. "I'll let her drive this. Appreciate it."

"That's the same as thanks," Blaise winked. "Have a good day!"

Jose watched as Blaise sashayed away, got in a black Camaro, and sped away. "She's a different kind of woman, isn't she?"

Dani snickered. "Yeah. She's great." She was nervous as hell. So nervous, it felt like her right leg was bouncing up and down. Like it used to when it was there. It felt so real that Dani had to look down to make sure the leg was really gone.

"You're accepting help now. That's good." Jose crossed his arms.

"Can you ever forgive me?" Dani asked, sounding like a child rather than the young adult she was now.

Jose gestured towards a bench a few feet away. "Mind if we sit for a moment?"

"Well, I kinda already am," Dani snorted, then cleared her throat. "Sorry."

Jose thumped her lightly on the shoulder. "I see you're still a smartass." He sat down and waited for Dani to situate herself. "It's me who should apologize," Jose said after a moment.

"Huh?"

"I promised your daddy I would watch over you," he explained. "I knew who you were. Well, um, not that you and my daughter were, you know. But . . ." Jose shifted uncomfortably. "Anyway, I should've predicted how Rita would react. I should've protected you like I promised your dad I would. I honestly didn't think she'd go as far as she did. For that, I'm sorry."

Dani took in everything Jose told her. She never knew her dad had that talk with Claire's dad. Maybe that's why he came looking for her every night. If she had known, would she have made different choices?

"It's not your fault, Mr. Oliver."

Jose raised a brow. "Mr. Oliver? When did we become so formal?"

When I started dating your daughter? Dani shrugged. "I dunno. But what I *do* know is that none of this is your fault. I should've trusted Claire that day and come home with her. I should've trusted you."

"Your mom messed you up, Dani. I can't blame you for running away. Or even feeling like everyone was against you."

Dani tapped her finger on the lever that controlled her wheelchair. Being with Jose made her miss her dad even more. "Do you think he'd still love me?" she asked quietly.

Jose knew exactly who Dani was talking about. "Yes," he answered without hesitation. "He loved you so much, Dani. He would talk about how you're the best of both worlds." Jose chuckled. "He was proud of daddy's little girl. And just as proud of the tomboy you were."

"Rita said if he'd known what I was, it would have killed him before the cancer did."

Jose snorted with disgust. "That woman lost her damn mind after your daddy died." He contemplated how much to tell Dani. After everything the poor girl was going through, should he be candid? Then realized that was precisely why she should know everything. *Why* she was now living a life without legs. "Rita never wanted kids, Dani. Nathan did, and she loved him enough to give him one. You. When Nathan got sick, Rita blamed everything except the cancer that your daddy had."

"Including me," Dani guessed. As hard as it was to hear that her mother *never* wanted her, it explained everything. Her mother had always been cold to her. It was nothing like it was between Claire and Karen. Still, Dani had thought her mother loved her. Wasn't that what mothers were supposed to do? Love their kids?

"Everything and everyone," Jose reiterated.

"I guess I didn't realize you and my dad were so close."

Jose smiled. "We bonded over our daughters."

"Do you, uh, think you could take me to the house sometime? I didn't get to take anything of dad's before I . . . left. I'd like *something* of his to keep with me, ya know?"

Jose frowned. "Claire didn't tell you."

"Tell me what?"

"Sweetheart, Rita sold the house and moved away a little more than a year ago."

"She-she moved? Did she tell you where she was going?"

Jose shook his head. "When she kicked you out, I went to the police and reported Rita for neglect. She got probation and had to pay a substantial fine. Once the probation was over, she left. If you want, I can try to help you find her."

Dani lowered her head. Her mother was gone. It was as if Dani never existed to Rita. Dani's father was dead. She had no family anymore. "Nah, it's okay. She probably wouldn't let me have anything anyway." She wiped a tear from her cheek. "I'm, uh, getting tired. Think you could take me home, er, to Claire's now?"

Jose leaned in and laid his hand on Dani's cast. "It's your home, too, Dani. And *we're* your family. Never doubt that. Whatever you need, we're here."

"Thanks, Mr. — thank you, pops."

CHAPTER TWENTY

"You really don't have to come in with me," Dani told Claire for the fifth time as Claire helped her out of the SUV.

Jose had kept his promise and let Claire use his car while she carted Dani around with her wheelchair. And now that Dani's cast was off, hopefully they wouldn't need it too much longer. She was *finally* getting her legs today. That already made her nervous. Having Claire watch terrified her. What if she couldn't stand up? What if she couldn't walk? What if she made herself look like a fool, wobbling around on two foreign objects that were supposed to take the place of her legs?

Claire rolled her eyes at Dani. It had been almost three weeks since Dani had moved in with her. For the most part, it was working out pretty well. However, there were those moments when Dani would get annoying with her "I don't want to be a burden" attitude. It's not that Claire couldn't understand why Dani would get like this. But having to constantly reassure Dani that she *wanted* to help could get tedious. Claire could only hope that once Dani had more autonomy, it would get better. That's why she wanted to be here for this monumental moment.

"How about you stop beating around the bush and just tell me what your problem is?" Claire huffed. She finally got Dani in the chair and strapped her in.

"I just . . ."

"No. I only want to hear how *you* truly feel. *Not* what you think *I'm* feeling."

Dani blew out a breath. "Fine. I don't want to look like a fool in front of you. Are you happy?"

"Well, now that you asked, no. I'm not happy. You have this distorted image of me in your head, Dani."

"No, I don't!"

"Yeah, you do. And, frankly, I'm sick of it. You know, I *barely* touched you last night in bed, and you flinched like I was trying to take advantage of you. You're so freakin' worried that how *you* feel about yourself is how *I* feel about you that you don't even give me a damn chance! You think I should find you disgusting or unsexy. You think I couldn't possibly be attracted to you. You think I'd freakin' laugh if you fell on your face in there with your new legs. Why in the hell would you want to *be* with someone as terrible and shallow as you think I am?"

Dani stared at Claire. Had she really been doing that? Yeah, she flinched last night. But that was because Claire's touch had surprised her. *Not* because Dani thought all those things about Claire. Right?

"I don't think that about you, Claire," Dani said softly.

"Really? Then what *do* you think, Dani? You asked Ellie to find me. You told me you needed me in your life."

"Which is true!"

"In what capacity, Dani?"

"I want it all, Claire! But you're the one who said you didn't know what we were to each other anymore," Dani reminded her. It was stupid, though, because Claire had been doing everything she could to find their way back to a version of what they used to be. And Dani was fucking it all up.

"At least I've been trying to figure it out. I've been trying to talk to you, to get you to open up to me. But you refuse. Now you don't want me here with you on one of the most important days of your life. Should I stop trying?"

"No," Dani whispered. "I'm sorry. I —"

"Forget it," Claire interrupted. God, she was trying to be empathetic with what Dani was going through. The truth was, though, she couldn't even begin to imagine it. Instead of getting upset, Claire needed to respect Dani's fears. That would be a lot easier if she weren't already miffed about the night before. "Just go in. I'll be back in an hour or so."

"Claire . . ." Dani's heart ached as she watched Claire round the SUV and get in. If Dani didn't get her act together, it would be Claire running away from her. For good.

Claire waited until a forlorn Dani disappeared inside the building before starting the car. She wanted to cry. She wanted to hit things. But most of all, she wanted to go and find Dani to tell her she was sorry. Claire killed the engine, putting the keys in her pocket. Her phone buzzed just as she got to the medical center's automatic door.

"How's the arm?" Dr. Andrews asked as he strapped a small prosthetic leg onto Dani.

Dani flexed her newly free arm. "It's still attached, and it works."

Dr. Andrews chuckled. "Well, that's a plus." He attached the right leg, then stood up. "You ready for this?"

"Nope." Dani sighed. "Yeah. I'm ready to start being more productive. These things okay in the shower?"

"Dani, slow down. I know you're excited to get your independence back, but it's going to take a good year or so for you to be able to walk on these things without assistance. Our first task is to get your balance, which will be difficult given your amputation was above the knee. We're starting you off in these shorties. Technically, they're called short prosthetic legs with training feet, which will aid us in helping stabilize your balance. They'll also help with building your muscles in your hips and residual limbs. We'll then gradually increase the height until, eventually, you'll progress to prosthetics legs that have what's called a microprocessor-controlled prosthetic knee joint."

"A what-what?" Dani's head was spinning. Damn, she should have *begged* Claire to come in with her! What made Dani think this would be as easy as getting legs and going? All the doctors told her it would be a journey. Even Hunter gave it to her straight about how hard it would be. But Dani had it in her thick skull that she would get the damn legs and be off running the next day. That was until this freakin' day got here, and she screwed up with Claire because of her insecurities.

Dr. Andrews smiled. "It acts as your knee joint. However, it can also compromise your stability. Now, you've been doing your physical therapy, but you'll still have difficulty bearing the weight of your body as you walk. You'll use a walker or crutches to help you until you get used to them."

"F-for how long?"

"That's up to you and how you do in therapy." Dr. Andrews laid a hand on Dani's shoulder. "I'm not going to lie to you, Dani. This is going to take a lot of time, grit, hope, support, and courage. I *implore* you to find someone to talk to about your emotions going through this."

"Like a shrink?"

"Yes."

Dani looked down at the shorties. *I'm going to look like an idiot in these.* "Can't I just put on the legs with the whatever and learn with them?"

"I highly recommend you don't, Dani. I've seen too many patients fail or give up because they wanted to skip this step. I've been doing this for more than fifteen years. Let me guide you, Dani. I'm here to make this transition as easy and as successful as possible."

"Do you think I'll be able to walk again? No wheelchair, no walker, or whatever? Seriously, doc. No mumbo jumbo, just an honest answer."

"Yeah, I do. I also think that having someone who has been through what you're about to go through would be extremely beneficial for you."

"Another amputee? Like, AA? Amputees Anonymous?" Dani scoffed.

"Not anonymous," Dr. Andrews frowned slightly. "They have no reason to be ashamed of who they are or what they've been through. Nor do you. But seeing someone who has been right where you are — who is now walking on their own — will give you the strength to keep going during the toughest times."

Dani nodded. "Yeah, okay." She took a deep breath. "Let's do this."

"Dani?"

Dani looked up sharply and saw Claire's red-rimmed eyes staring back at her. Immediately, Dani felt like a freakin' asshole for making Claire cry. Dani also wanted to sprint to Claire, hug her, and express just how much Dani needed her.

"Claire, I'm so sorry. I should've . . ."

"Dani, it's Ellie." Claire sniffled and wiped her nose with some tissue she had found in her dad's car. The phone call from Piper had carried with it sad news that Claire would now have to burden Dani with. "There's been an accident."

Dani's brows furrowed. "What accident? Where is she? I-is she okay?"

Claire slowly shook her head. "A car accident. She's in a coma, baby."

The world stopped for Dani right then. Ellie had become like a mother figure to Dani. Hell, Ellie was more of a mother to Dani than Rita ever was. And now . . .

"No," Dani whispered as though speaking loud would break some magical hold this world had on Ellie. "She has to be okay. She *has* to!"

"Ready?" Claire unbuckled her seatbelt, poised to get out of the car. Dani's focus was completely lost after Claire told her the news about Ellie. Even Dr. Andrews agreed that Dani wouldn't be able to concentrate on her therapy in the state she was in.

"No," Dani croaked. She couldn't stop crying. What if Ellie didn't make it? What if she never came out of the coma? No matter how positive Dani tried to be, the negativity overruled her brain. Then there was this freakin' hospital.

Being back here made Dani feel anxious and scared. "I can't go in there."

"What? You said you wanted to visit . . ."

"I know! But I can't!" Dani's head fell back onto the headrest, and she let out a long, heavy sigh. "Sorry, I didn't mean to snap at you. It's just being here makes my legs hurt."

Claire frowned. "Huh?"

"I still feel them sometimes. Pain, itching, the weight of them. Freaks me out. But when I'm close to this hospital, the pain seems to be more intense. I know it's all in my head." Dani shrugged.

"I've read about that. Phantom pain," Claire explained. "A lot of amputees have experienced it, so I don't think it's just in your head."

"It's, like, a real thing? Damn. I thought I was just crazy." Dani scratched her head. "Wait, you read about this stuff?"

"Yes. It's always good to be educated. Plus, I like to read."

"Is there, like, a cure or something? Or am I gonna have to live with this shit forever?"

Claire turned in her seat to face Dani. She knew Dani was stalling. Dani may not be able to go in the hospital, but Claire didn't think she could leave just yet, either. Though Claire was worried about Ellie — not to mention Jessie and Hunter — she had to think about Dani's wellbeing, too.

"Is it a lot of pain?" Claire asked Dani.

Dani shrugged. "Sometimes. A lot of times, it's just a throbbing. But, times like now, it can be shooting pain. Like someone is stabbing me or something."

Claire nodded. "I read that's common. If I remember correctly, some doctors say it could be mixed signals from the brain and spinal cord. I don't know if I understood everything the article was saying, but I think they do some kind of test like an MRI."

The thought of being in a machine like that made Dani's eye twitch. "Did the article say anything about it going away, though?"

"I think that's something you should talk to Dr. Andrews about your options, Dani." Claire could tell her answer wasn't satisfying. "It said treatments could be anything from medication to surgery."

"Surgery?! I don't want another surgery ever again!" Dani shivered. "What if they end up taking my dang arms!"

Claire chuckled. "Dani, Hunter didn't *mistakenly* take your legs."

"I know, but still. What if Hunter doesn't do the surgery because she's worried about Ellie and the doctor that takes her place is incompetent?"

Claire's eyebrows lifted. "Have you thought about this often?"

"No. Maybe. Whatever. Surgery requires being in the hospital, and I don't want that. If I just stay away from the freakin' hospital, my legs won't hurt. That much."

Claire shook her head. She wished she had paid more attention to the phantom pain article she read. *I guess I have more research to do.* "Okay. So, I'm guessing you still don't want to go up and visit Ellie?"

"I do, Claire. I don't think I can go in there, though. I — I can't see her like that. I can blame my freakin' legs or craziness all day long. But the truth is, as scared as I am of being here, I'm even more terrified of seeing her lying in a hospital bed."

Claire sighed softly. She certainly didn't blame Dani. Claire was worried about how *she'd* handle seeing Ellie so helpless. With everything Dani was dealing with, that could be the one thing that pushed her over the proverbial edge to insanity. "Okay. I'll take you home and text Piper."

"You're disappointed in me, aren't you?"

"No, I'm not, Dani. I actually understand. Being here doesn't bring back the best of memories. Though this is where you met Ellie. And where we found each other again. One day, I hope we can replace bad memories — like those of losing your legs — with the good."

"Not if Ellie doesn't make it," Dani sniffled. "I'll never come back to this hospital again if something happens to her."

"We're not going to think like that. Positive thoughts. I know it sounds silly, but I don't want to put that negativity out in the universe. Okay?"

"Yeah, okay. Maybe I'll be able to visit another day."

"Whenever you're ready, just let me know."

Chapter Twenty-One

"Can you get me a coke?"

Claire glanced up from her book and saw Dani sitting there on the couch, staring at the TV. Claire's last nerve nearly exploded. "You know where it is."

Dani frowned and gestured at her legs. "Really, Claire?" Yeah, she had on the "shorties", but she still wasn't steady on them.

"Really, Dani?" Claire shot back. "You're supposed to be walking on those things, doing your exercises. Yet, for nearly two weeks, you've done nothing but sit on your ass."

"These *things* are freakin' stupid!" Dani emphasized her point by unstrapping one of the shorties and throwing it across the room.

Claire closed her book with a snap and tossed it on the chair next to her. "When are you going to let go of your goddamn ego? I have been showering you, helping you to the bathroom, and *this* is what you're embarrassed about? Having to walk in these short, *training* legs in front of me? That's such bullshit, Dani! I have been trying to be understanding with your mood swings, but you've gone too far. People who *barely* knew you spent time and money trying to help you! This is how you repay them. By giving up and throwing expensive equipment that *they* paid for across the room. This is how you repay *me*?!"

"You don't understand what this is like, Claire!"

"You're right. I don't. But do you know what I *do* understand? What it's like to have a girlfriend who expected me to wait on her hand and foot. I got with Cris because she reminded me of you. Don't make me leave you because you remind me of her."

Claire's words were like a slap in the face to Dani. Or more like a bucket of ice-cold water over the head. After Ellie's accident, a more profound depression set in for Dani. Even after she found out Ellie had woken up from her coma, Dani couldn't find the motivation to do the work she knew she needed to do. She was letting everyone down. Especially Claire. But it was like she couldn't hear Ellie's encouraging voice anymore. There was no special pie to get Dani through this. She wasn't sure *anything* could get her through this.

"Where are you going?" Dani asked when Claire got up and put her coat on.

"To visit Ellie." Dani still hadn't been able to go to the hospital, so Claire always went alone and would come home with a report for Dani. The one thing she hadn't told Dani, yet, was that Ellie was paralyzed. No one knew if it would be permanent, but Claire had been afraid that the news would send Dani into even more of a tailspin. Claire now wondered if she had been upfront with Dani if it would have motivated Dani to be more diligent with her therapy. That was her desperation talking, but Claire needed things to change before she couldn't hang on any longer. Claire looked back at Dani once she got to the door. "One day, Ellie is going to need you the way you needed her."

Dani's brows furrowed, and she nearly laughed, which would *not* be good when Claire was this pissed at her. But Dani couldn't imagine a situation where Ellie would need her.

"What are you talking about?"

"She's paralyzed, Dani. Maybe I should have told you before, but I'm telling you now. After everything Ellie has done for you, don't you think you owe it to her to do everything she knew you could do?"

With that parting blow, Claire walked out and closed the door behind her. She stood there for a full minute fighting back the tears. That wasn't how Claire had wanted to break the news to Dani. Hell, nothing that was happening in their lives right now was what she wanted. But this is what life had handed them. It was their job to make the best out of it. If Claire only knew how to do that without losing her mind. She took a deep breath. Maybe visiting Ellie would give her some clarity.

Inside the apartment, Dani sat motionless. Ellie was paralyzed. How was that possible? Ellie was a force. She was strong. She was good. How could something like this happen to someone like her? Losing her legs was devastating for Dani, yeah, but at least *that* she could understand. Dani was a nobody. She had been homeless and did things she wasn't proud of. Maybe it was punishment. Maybe it was karma. Hell, perhaps it was just meant to be. But Ellie? Ellie Montgomery deserved nothing but good.

Dani fixed the shorty back on her stump. This was it. *This* was the moment Dani got her head out of her ass and became the person those around her believed she could be. If not for herself, then for Ellie. Dani shook her head.

"No, I have to do it for me first," she said aloud in the empty apartment. Dani scooted to the edge of the sofa. It was almost funny how far away the floor seemed to be. "Then for Claire." She used her arm strength to help lower herself until her training prosthetics hit the carpet. "Then for Ellie." Dani took her first step. Second step. Third.

Claire had set up an area in the small living room for Dani to do her exercises. Every day Dani was supposed to do a series of activities that were designed to strengthen her hips, arms, and leg muscles. The stronger she got, the easier it would be to maneuver in real prosthetic legs that wouldn't make her feel so self-conscious. *When are you going to let go of your goddam ego?*

"Now," Dani vowed. She stepped up on the stepper Claire had bought for her, using the chair next to it for added balance. It was uncomfortable, but nothing she couldn't handle. Going back down was a little more daunting even though the step was mere inches off the ground. "Do it, Dani," she commanded herself. Her hand never left the chair. Her heart skipped a beat. But she stepped down backward — one of the more natural ways the therapist taught her.

She wobbled slightly but held her balance. Dani repeated the motion several times before stopping to catch her breath. Her stubs were beginning to get sore, and she could feel sweat beginning to form. Dani would have to take the shorties off to dry and clean them soon or risk getting a rash. She smiled, proud of herself for listening to her doctor. Before she did that, however, Dani needed water. She looked over at the kitchen. It was over a mile away. She rolled her eyes at her exaggerating self. It was literally less than ten steps for someone with legs. For Dani, it would be more, but it was time she started proving herself to Claire. It took her the better part of ten minutes, but Dani made it to the fridge.

"Well, you look about as good as I feel."

Claire looked up sharply, right into Joselyn Cohan's smiling eyes. "Ms. Cohan!"

"Ah, ah. I thought we agreed you'd call me Jos?"

Claire blushed. "Sorry. I, um, was reading the new stuff earlier."

Jos raised a brow. "I hope that's not what put you in this mood. May I?" she gestured to the booth across from Claire.

"O-of course." Claire sat up a little straighter. She wished now that she had brushed her hair. Or put a little makeup on. Had she known she'd be face to face with Joselyn Cohan — again — she would have. It almost pissed Claire off that Joselyn had a messy bun and little makeup herself and still looked glamorous. "And, no. The new chapters are incredible. I love where you're going with the story. I didn't see that twist coming at all!"

Jos grinned. "Good." She ordered a coffee and a slice of the "pie of the day" when the waitress came by. "Want to talk about what's bothering you, then?"

"Oh! No. I mean, you just said you weren't feeling well . . ."

"Actually, what I said was you look like I feel. And you look lost. Besides, my stuff is all writing-related. I get in these moods where I hate everything I'm writing. So, instead of deleting chapter after chapter, I came here to Ellie's Diner. The pies seem to help my concentration." Jos's eyebrows furrowed then. "Except, lately, something seems to be a little off. They're still delicious, just different."

Claire swallowed the lump in her throat. "That's because the owner, Ellie, is in the hospital."

"Oh my. Is she alright?"

A tear managed to escape and roll down Claire's cheek. "She was run off the road and was in a coma for what seemed like an eternity. Now she's paralyzed, and we don't know if it's permanent or not." Claire pressed her lips together. "I don't know why I just told you that."

Jos smiled kindly. "Because I asked, and you needed someone to listen."

"I guess. I mean, Ellie is like a second mother to me. And like a *real* mother to Dani. Which means Dani has all but shut down over the news. She won't do her exercises. She's depressed, she's moody. I don't know what to do anymore. Or if I'm enough for her."

"I don't know Dani, Claire, but I've gotten to know you a little better over the past few weeks. I can't imagine you not being up for any challenge. But when it comes to relationships, it can't be a one-way street. It should never be about if *you* are enough for her. It should be about how you work together to be strong enough for each other."

Another tear. Claire wiped it away with her napkin. "It's all so much, you know. When I was a senior in high school, I had a plan. I had it all worked out in my mind about how life would go. And then, one day, the ground fell out from under me."

Jos sat back when the waitress came back with her order.

After a quiet "thank you," she focused again on Claire. "In the writing world, there are planners and pansters. Some of my colleagues are incredible planners. They have everything outlined down to the smallest detail. Often, they run into a snag or two as the story progresses. Why? Because they'll inevitably change their mind at some point about *something,* and that could throw off everything they had planned. The ones who don't pull their hair out are the ones who can roll with those changes. As if they were planned all along."

"How do they do that? If they mapped it all out, aren't they disappointed when it doesn't turn out the way they wanted?"

"No, because they understand that what they changed made the story better." Jos took a sip of her coffee, studying Claire over the rim. "Your story is in the angst portion right now. But try to imagine what life would have been like had Dani not been kicked out. You both were in high school. You had college to look forward to. Dani had another year to go, right?"

Claire nodded, dumbfounded that Jos remembered everything Claire had told her in Anne's office that day. God, that day. Claire had thought she was going to lose her job. Instead, she was now working *for* Jos permanently. *A change to the plan that made the story better*, Claire thought silently.

"So," Jos continued. "Imagine if things had gone exactly as you had planned. Would Dani still be in your life?"

Claire automatically wanted to say a resounding yes but stopped. "I don't know." She frowned. "Dani was afraid I'd find someone else in college. Her ego gets in the way of her common sense sometimes. It's impossible to know if she would have stayed with me while being insecure about my feelings for her."

Jos slapped the table, causing Claire to jump. "That's my

point! It's *impossible* to know what's going to happen. I love my planner buddies, but I'm a panster for just that reason. Whatever is in my mind one day could be totally forgotten or totally skewed because of everyday experiences. Each day we become someone different. It could be a minuscule change or a colossal one. But it's still a change. We have to be ready to accept that in our lives, or we're left staring at a blank page waiting for the story to get back on track."

Claire sat back with a thud. "No wonder you're an excellent writer." She tapped her blunt nails on the table. "So, Dani and I have our second chance? How do I not pull my hair out? How do I roll with all these changes that feel like the ground is crumbling again?"

"You remember that this *is* your second chance. Keep talking to Dani. Help her see that the mistakes from the past can be learned from. Because if they're not, they're doomed to be repeated. And *you*, Claire, adjust what you think and feel to include what Dani is going through mentally as well as physically. I know that may be incredibly difficult since neither of us knows what it's like to lose a limb. Let alone two. It may also be hard to rein in your frustrations. But if you're serious about Dani — and I think you are — you'll find a way."

"How do you know so much about this stuff? Were you, like, a psychiatrist in a previous life or something?"

Jos laughed heartily. "No. though, speaking of psychiatrists, have you or Dani thought about seeing one?"

"I can't even get Dani to talk to you. Or me!" Claire sighed. "I do think she needs it, though."

"Not just her, Claire." Jos saw the skepticism in Claire's eyes. Perhaps a little fear as well. "Listen, that's just my non-expert advice. You both need to do what's right for you *when* it's right. Just know that I'll always be here to listen. And not only for content for my next book." Jos winked.

Claire's eyes widened. Then she saw Jos's mischievous smile. "I don't know if you're serious or not."

"The curse of being friends with a writer."

Claire held her breath as she let herself into the apartment. She had been feeling a bit better after her impromptu visit with Jos. Claire was glad she had decided to go to Ellie's Diner after finding out Ellie wasn't up for visitors at the hospital. When Claire was at the diner, she felt a little closer to Ellie. Plus, there was pie. Pie always helped. However, the closer she got to the apartment, the more anxious she got. What if Dani was still mad at her? Or worse, what if Dani left.

Just inside the door, Claire stood there and listened. The only light on was the one over the kitchen counter. The TV was off. No noise from the bathroom. Claire looked at her watch. It was only nine o'clock. Dani was usually up watching TV or playing video games until she couldn't keep her eyes open any longer. It had been annoying for Claire, who had to get up out of a deep sleep to help Dani with her nighttime routine. Then she found out Dani had terrifying nightmares when she tried to sleep when she wasn't completely exhausted. So, Claire adjusted.

I adjusted. Claire smiled to herself. That was good news!

Well, good news only if Dani was still here. And then she heard it. Dani's soft — cute — snore. Dani was here! And sleeping. Claire rechecked her watch to make sure she saw it right the first time. **9:07 pm**. This was new. She tiptoed to the counter to put her keys down so she could check on Dani when she saw the note. No. Notes. A stack of them. Claire picked up the Post-It first.

Claire, I'm sorry. I wish I could be better at sharing my feelings. I wanted you to know that I did all my exercises tonight. I even took a shower by myself. I probably should have waited on that just in case anything happened. But I did it, and everything is fine-ish. Anyway, I wrote you letters while I was, you know, out there. I thought maybe they would help you understand me a little better. Or maybe not hate me? Love, Dani

"I *don't* hate you," Claire whispered. Then she frowned. "Fine-ish?" A tiny part of her wanted to rush into the bedroom to make sure Dani was okay. An even smaller part wanted to go into the bathroom to see what kind of mess was in there. But another snore told her Dani was just fine. Whatever was going on in the bathroom could wait. Right now, Claire had some reading to do.

CHAPTER TWENTY-TWO

I screwed up, Claire. Big time. I don't even know why I did it. I knew it was wrong. But I'm so tired of being out here. I'm afraid to go to the shelter now. After what I've done, I don't think I'd be welcome. That means, if I get hungry, I have to find my food in the dumpster. There's this restaurant not too far from here that throws out, like, a ton of food. I mean, it all goes in the dumpster before I can get it, but at least it's something, you know?

I'm waiting for the day Angel kicks me out of the tent. I deserve it after what I've done. God, I'm such a freakin' idiot! I believed Viper when she told me I could make some cash and get off the streets just by being a stupid mule or whatever. I shouldn't have trusted her. Angel warned me. But goddamn it, I don't want to piss in a can in the alley anymore, Claire! I don't want to wipe coffee grounds and who knows what else off my food before I eat it! I don't want to be freezing in the tent, wishing I had you to snuggle up with in the winter. And in the summer . . . I can't handle the heat anymore!

None of that matters, though. I hurt someone I cared about. I mean, Beard looked out for me. If I'd known that Viper was feeding him the drugs I had been getting for her, I never would have done it. I swear! There are, like, three sure-fire ways of getting money out here that I know of — panhandle, prostitute, or push. I could barely make a buck panhandling. No fuckin' way I was going to sleep with some dude. So I chose to push the drugs. I thought it was the least evil of the three. Until I saw Beard foaming at the mouth. He almost died, Claire. Because of me. I don't care that I didn't physically hand him the drugs. I brought them to Viper. I should have known. She's a Landlord. I worked with the enemy. And now, I have to live with what I've done. I don't know if I can.

I told Viper I was done. She said it wasn't that easy. If I didn't run drugs, I'd have to pay in some other way. Maybe I should just let your dad find me. Jail has to be better than this, right? I mean, it can't be worse. At least I'd have three meals a day. And a fuckin' toilet. Maybe a mattress. Claire, it's getting to the point where I don't care what Viper or her gang does to me. I'm so tired. I've made so many mistakes that I can't undo. The biggest one was leaving you. I have nothing else to go on for. Sorry this is getting so freakin' depressing. I miss you. I miss my life. I wish I knew how to fix this.

"Claire?" Dani shook Claire's shoulder as gently as she could, but Claire still woke with a start.

"What! Oh." Claire cleared her throat and rubbed her face. "Are you ready to go to bed?"

Dani smiled. "I just got up. It's morning, Claire. You must've fallen asleep out here on the couch."

"Huh?" Claire squinted her eyes against the sun that was now pouring into the apartment. When she sat up from her prone position, papers crinkled beneath her. *Oh, yeah.* She had sat down on the couch to read the letters Dani had written her. Twice. Her heart ached for everything Dani had been through.

Each letter renewed her disgust for Rita and her admiration for Dani. Dani may have done things she wasn't proud of, but Claire couldn't blame her for them. Dani did what she had to do to survive. Claire could feel sorrow for Beard, and hatred for Viper, but she still couldn't condemn Dani. Besides, Dani did that enough for both of them.

"I woke up, and you weren't in bed. I thought maybe you hadn't come home," Dani confessed quietly.

Claire was still trying to clear the sleep out of her brain. She could definitely use some coffee. "I didn't think you'd still be here." She frowned. "I didn't mean that."

"Yeah, you did. It's okay. I get it. I'm sorry." Dani took a step back.

"Wait. I didn't mean to say it like that. Look, I can't be sorry for what I said last night. It needed to be said. I needed to get it out before it ate me up. But I could've been, I don't know, nicer about it all?"

"Nah, you gave me the kick in the ass I needed." Dani lifted her leg. "See? I'm wearing them. Getting my steps in," she grinned. "I called Dr. Andrews. I have an appointment in about an hour. Then I'll be going to my first meeting."

Claire's brows furrowed. "Meeting?"

"Yeah. Dr. Andrews suggested I talk to others who have been through what I'm going through. I mean, I love you and appreciate everything you're doing for me, Claire. But . . ."

"But I don't understand," Claire finished for Dani. "I think you're doing the right thing, Dani. You need more than I can give you. As long as you understand I'm still going to be here."

"God, I hope so!" Dani chuckled. "I kinda made a mess in the bathroom. So, I could still use your help in there. And, ya know, everywhere else. These meetings are designed, I think, to give me the courage to keep going. But I still need you. I hope my ego and I didn't push you away for good."

"I told you I'm going to be here. For as long as you want me." Claire picked up one of the letters. "I read all of these," she said softly. "I would think of you every day, Dani. I would wonder where you were, what you had to do to survive, if you were eating. Where you were sleeping." She smoothed the crumpled paper, treating it as if it were a treasure. To Claire, it was. "These answered all of my questions. But left me with one."

"Oh?" Dani had thought the letters had been highly informative. What more could she tell Claire?

"Was it an accident, Dani?" Claire held out the last letter Dani had written.

Dani, however, didn't need to read it to remember what she wrote. She knew how it sounded. "No."

"Did Viper do this to you?" Claire's hands began to shake when Dani merely lifted a shoulder. "Say the words, Dani."

"Yeah."

"Did you let her?"

Dani hesitated. Just like she did that night. "*I don't know,*" she barely whispered. "I saw the car coming towards me. Maybe I had time to jump out of the way, but I honestly don't know, Claire. It's one of the things that haunts my dreams." She leaned against the coffee table. "I saw her face behind the wheel, closing in on me. I saw the cruel smile. They say your life flashes before you in times like that." Dani shook her head. "But that's not what happened. Viper turned into a laughing Noah. Noah turned into Rita, who had no love in her eyes whatsoever for her only daughter. And then it all happened so fast. Rita's face disappeared. I don't remember the impact. But I do remember waking up in that goddamn hospital wondering why I was still alive."

"Is that why you were so angry with Hunter? Not because she took your legs, but because she saved your life?"

Dani nodded. "I shouldn't be here, Claire. Not after everything I've done."

Claire reached out and took Dani's hand. "All of this blame does not belong on your shoulders, Dani. You didn't sell the drugs, and you didn't force Beard to take them. That was Viper. You weren't ashamed of who you were, but others couldn't understand it. That was Noah. And you weren't out there because you wanted to be. That was Rita. Give blame to those who deserve it."

"I promised Angel I wouldn't get involved with Viper. I betrayed her. I promised my dad I would make him proud, and I betrayed him. I promised to love you and left. I betrayed you."

"That's quite the burden, Dani. Circumstances cause us to make choices. Some of those choices are good. Others are complete mistakes. But you've done nothing that can't be forgiven. I think your dad would be proud of how you've survived against all the odds. I don't know Angel, but if she's as good as you say she is, she'll forgive you for trying to find a better life." Claire got down on her knees in front of Dani, and they were eye to eye. "You found me again when you didn't have to. I love you, Dani. And I forgive you."

Tears flowed freely down Dani's cheeks. It was amazing what the words "I forgive you" could do to a damaged heart. Dani's downward spiral began when her father died. Parts of her were chipped away with each taunt from her bullies. Her hope faded when her mother threw her out like a piece of trash. Was love and forgiveness from Claire enough to heal her? Probably not, but it was a hell of a good start. The rest was up to Dani.

"Thank you," she said with a shaky voice. "I think I needed that."

"I wish I could have given it to you sooner," Claire confessed.

"You needed to know everything before you could do that," Dani figured. "I wanted to give you these letters before. I was scared."

Claire nodded in understanding. "Jos told me last night that we change every day. No matter how big or small that change is, it affects us. I think I fully understand what she meant now. I'm ready to start over with you, Dani. If you are?"

Dani wiped tears away with the back of her hand. "Yeah, I think I am. For real now." Tentatively, she leaned in for a kiss, then stopped abruptly. "Jos? I thought you went to visit Ellie."

"I did, but Ellie wasn't up for visitors. So, I went to the diner. It makes me feel close to Ellie, ya know?" Dani nodded. "Jos just happened to show up there with a plethora of good advice."

"I don't know what that word means," Dani frowned.

Claire giggled. "A lot, babe. She said a lot of good things that made me think. And she made me realize that I can't be everything to you. We have to complement each other's strengths and weaknesses so that we can grow together."

Dani's eyebrows raised. "Wow. That sounds pretty smart. Maybe I should rethink talking to her about my experiences out there."

"I think you should, but you do what you feel is right. I will back you no matter what." Claire thought for a second. "You could always give her your letters."

Dani shook her head. "Those are only for you." She shrugged. "Who knows, it may be good for me to talk to her. I don't think I'm ready for a shrink, yet."

"Sounds like the beginning of a plan," Claire grinned. "Now, you were about to kiss me."

"Right." Dani leaned in again. And stopped. Again. "Sorry. I just have to know one thing."

"What?"

"I think that, uh, making love . . . it'll be different with me. For me."

Claire smiled. "You called it making love. That's the first time you've said that. So, yeah, it will be different. But, like everything else, we'll roll with the changes. Now," she grabbed Dani's t-shirt and pulled her close. "Kiss me."

Claire beeped the lock of the SUV twice, then once more for added measure. Twenty minutes before, she was dropping Dani off at her appointment. The plan then was to head back home to finish the new chapters of Jos's book. But Claire's plan took a detour. *Change the plan to make the story better.* The moment she stepped out of the truck, however, she wondered what the hell she was doing. She was entirely out of her depth here. Not to mention scared shitless.

"You lost?"

Claire spun around at the raspy voice. Fuck, she wished she had remembered to bring pepper spray or something! "Um, no. I'm, uh . . ."

"Lost. Go home, little girl." The hooded figure turned and walked away.

Claire's brows furrowed, and her lips tightened. *Rude!* "Listen! I'm . . ." *Wait. Hoodie. Woman. Could this be?* "Angel?"

The woman stopped. "I know you?"

"No. But you know Dani. Or Kid."

Angel lowered her head and hoped to hell nothing had happened to the kid. When she turned back, the young woman with a pixie cut was staring at her. No fear now. Just determination in her young, innocent eyes.

"Why are you here?"

"You're Angel, right? The one they say takes care of people here?"

Angel cocked her head to one side. "I'm the one they call Angel, yes. And you are?"

"Claire. Dani's girlfriend."

A smile played at Angel's lips. Not that Claire could see her face. Dani had a new protector. Perhaps this one would do a better job.

"What can I do for you, Dani's girlfriend?"

"You failed her," Claire said abruptly. "She almost died. Where were you?"

The smile faded, replaced by grief born of guilt. "If I could change the events of that night, I would," Angel said as softly as her rough voice would allow. "But I can't. I'm sorry."

Claire sighed. "No, I'm sorry. I didn't come here to accuse you or make this your fault."

"Then why did you come here?"

"So maybe you could make it right somehow. Dani knows who did this to her, but she won't go to the authorities." Claire gestured to the horror that was Skid Row. "These poor people have it hard enough. They don't need to be terrorized by gangs like the Landlords."

What the hell did this kid want? Angel did her best to protect the people she *lived* with. But . . . "I'm just one person, Claire."

"So is Viper."

Angel's jaws clenched. This was the first time her suspicions had been confirmed. Hearsay on the street didn't get her far, but if Dani remembered, that's all Angel needed.

"Make her go to the cops," Angel ordered.

Claire laughed mirthlessly. "Do you think I'd be here if I could do that? She refuses. She doesn't want to put anyone else in danger."

Angel inhaled sharply and began to pace. "Hardhead son-of-a- . . ."

"I've tried that. It doesn't work. So, I'm asking you, Angel. Make Viper pay for what she did to Dani."

"What is it you think I can do?" Angel knew exactly what she was going to do, but she was curious how far this woman would go.

"I don't know! Listen, I promised Dani I wouldn't go to the police. But I didn't promise I wouldn't come to see you. And you aren't bound to the same oath. Viper did this. Now you know. Do what you will with that information. Just, please, do *something*."

"You have a set, coming down here to snitch on a gang

member," Angel stated with a healthy amount of respect. She held her gloved hand out to Claire. "I promise I will do *something*. Deal?"

Claire didn't hesitate to take the hand in front of her. "Deal. Thank you."

"How is she?" Angel asked before letting Claire's hand go.

"Adjusting. Starting a new chapter now."

"Good. Help her close this one forever," Angel suggested.

Claire shook her head. "That won't happen. It'll always be a part of her. She's coming to terms with what happened here. Maybe one day you'll see her again when she's ready to face the past so she can conquer it. Please consider forgiving her."

Angel stepped back as though she'd been slapped. "Forgive her? For what?"

"She feels she betrayed you and Beard and was punished for it. Though, in my book, the punishment didn't fit her so-called crime."

"Jesus. We all make decisions, mostly selfishly. I can't condemn the Kid for wanting a better life than the one she had out here. She was offered a false world and fell for it. We've all done that before. It's how we learn. As for Beard, he, too, made his choices. That had nothing to do with Kid. There's nothing to forgive, Claire."

Claire smiled genuinely. She had no intention of telling Dani that she had come out here. But, if she didn't, Dani wouldn't know that Angel held no ill will. This was yet another change that could make the story better. At least that's how Claire hoped Dani would feel about what Claire had done on her behalf.

"Is there a way you could keep me updated on the outcome of whatever happens here?" Claire asked hopefully.

"You want confirmation of the hit you just put out on a gang member?"

"What! I didn't . . . that's not . . . no!"

Angel laughed. "Calm down, girl. I'm messing with you. Viper will be dealt with in a *legal* way. I'm not a killer."

There was something about the way Angel said that last sentence that made the hairs on Claire's neck stand up. "O-okay. Um, could I give you my number then?" She reached for her purse, then remembered she had left it in the truck.

Angel handed her an iPhone. One of the newest versions. Claire would take the time to wonder about that later. When she was safe in her apartment and away from the stench that had been Dani's life for two years. Claire added her contact information, tagging herself as "Dani's girlfriend" for Angel's amusement.

"Do better than I did," Angel called out as Claire got in her vehicle.

"We all do our best," Claire said with a gentle smile. A smile that stayed with her all the way home.

Chapter Twenty-Three

"Are you sure about this?"

Claire sighed. "Will you stop asking me that? Yes! I'm sure!"

"Sorry! It's just, this is the first time we've done this since . . ."

"Believe me, I'm aware."

Claire took a deep, cleansing breath. Her nervousness had nothing to do with Dani and everything to do with her irrational insecurities. It was silly. Ever since the letters came to light, life had been different. Claire and Dani had changed. They remembered what it had been like between them before the world changed. They found that spark. That special bond.

Intimacy between them had been a learning experience. And a journey. Anxiety often won over when the couple would try being together. At the advice of a fellow amputee, Claire and Dani took it slow and steady. They were told to start by holding hands and cuddling. It may have seemed small to anyone on the outside looking in. But to the young couple, it significantly built their trust and comfort with each other. They would even talk about what they feared, what they expected, and what they needed. That part was probably the hardest for them both.

Eventually, cuddling would turn into touching. Touching turned into kissing. Kissing became a need — a want. The first time Claire and Dani made love was liberating. They spent the night learning and exploring this new territory. What worked for them. What didn't. Dani was much more adventurous than

Claire imagined she would be. And Claire soaked up each tidbit of information Dani gave, whether it was verbal or not. If a position was uncomfortable, they changed it. If Dani felt pain, they tried something new. The biggest lesson they learned was that legs were not necessary to have an amazing, active sex life.

However, showering in the harsh lights of the bathroom was a different animal altogether. That's where they were now. Dani was standing in the steaming shower in all her glory. Her shorties — now a couple of inches taller — gave her the perfect height in her opinion—eye to boob. Now, if Claire would just get in with her.

"What are your fears, Claire?"

Claire giggled. "We've become that couple, haven't we? The "let's talk about it" couple."

Dani shrugged. "Whatever gets you to take off that robe and get in here with me. You know you're beautiful, right?"

"In the dim light."

Dani rolled her eyes. "I've seen you in all kinds of light. There's not a part of you I don't love." She sat on the handy little bench and studied her girlfriend. "Is it ironic that now *you're* the one with the body insecurities when we spent, like, a ton of time getting me through mine?"

Claire pursed her lips. She recalled everything she ever said to Dani to ease her self-doubt. How Claire loved Dani for more than the outside appearance.

"I'm being silly, aren't I?" Claire fiddled with the tie of her robe.

"No. You're being human. Plus, you're used to being in here with me with clothes on. Maybe it's just going to take some time to switch gears from care-taker to lover here in the shower?"

The side of Claire's mouth quirked into a half-smile. "You really are learning a lot in your meetings."

"Well, if I weren't, they'd be a waste of time." Dani made a silly face.

That silly face was exactly what Claire needed to shed her fears. And her robe. Just as she was stepping into the shower, the doorbell rang.

"You have *got* to be kidding me!" Dani groaned. "Don't put that back on!" she said when Claire bent to pick up her robe. "They'll go away if we just ignore them."

"Dani."

"Claire! We just got to the good part!"

"Look at it this way; I got through the hard part. Now, when we're alone again, we can move forward."

"But we're alone now!" Dani called out as Claire walked out of the bathroom. She sat there, sulking. And soaking. If she were lucky, Claire would get rid of whomever rudely interrupted them and come back. Unless it was . . . Dani's eyes bugged out. "Oh, shit!" she blurted out. What if it was Claire's parents? Dani was scooting off the bench when Claire came back in.

"Hey, you need to get dressed, babe."

"Don't tell me it's your parents," Dani mumbled.

"No, it's Jessie. Ellie needs you."

"I interrupted something. I'm so sorry!" Jessie said when Claire came back into the room.

"No, you didn't."

"Yes, she did!" Dani called out from the bathroom. Once she was dried off and covered, Dani made her way into the living room. "But since it's for Ellie, I'll forgive you," she grinned.

Jessie tried smiling back, but her heart was hurting. Ellie had been acting differently since the accident. She was no longer the happy, positive woman that raised Jessie. She wasn't the same person who helped Dani come to terms with losing her legs and reunited Dani with Claire.

"I need you to talk to Mom, Dani."

"Why me? I'm sure she has people who are much smarter than me that can be more help." Dani perched herself on the couch next to Claire, their thighs touching. She was hoping to draw some strength off her girlfriend.

Jessie shook her head. "No one knows what she's going through. Except you. With everyone else, she's just moody. Mom snaps at me for the littlest things. Which I could understand, you know? This has been traumatic for her. Running is her thing when she's anxious or sad. She can't do that now. She can't even bake or cook anymore. But that doesn't mean it doesn't hurt when she's hostile with me. She's never been that way before."

"Maybe Ellie just needs time to adjust," Claire suggested, noting Dani's stiff body next to her. She couldn't imagine how this news of Ellie was affecting Dani's newfound confidence.

Jessie stood up and began to pace. "Maybe. I don't know. We've tried everything. We don't even say anything when she yells at us. We just turn the other cheek, then cry when we're alone. But it's getting so hard to keep the façade. Or the hope that this will pass. Hunter is taking the brunt of Mom's wrath, and she doesn't deserve that. Even Blaise, Mom's *best* friend, has stopped coming by so often. God, *all* of mom's friends have slowly stopped visiting because they think it's upsetting for Mom, and that's why she acts out. But it's more than that, I just know it. Please, Dani. I want my mom back."

"Dani will go talk to Ellie," Claire announced.

"Wait, what?" Dani hopped down. Her pacing wasn't as fast as Jessie's, but that didn't stop her. "Shouldn't that be *my* decision?"

"You're saying no?" Jessie asked dejectedly.

"No, I'm not saying no," Dani responded quickly. She didn't want Jessie to think she didn't want to help. Dani just didn't know if she *could* help. And that's what was giving her pause. "I . . ." Instead of finishing her sentence, Dani escaped to the bedroom.

Claire sighed. "I'll go talk to her. Don't go anywhere."

Jessie plopped down in the chair she had occupied before her distressed pacing. "If you can get Dani to talk to Mom, I'll cook dinner for both of you for two weeks!"

Claire chuckled. "That's not necessary. Unless you cook like Ellie," she winked. "I'll be right back."

Claire found Dani standing next to the bed, clothes laid out. That was a good sign, at least.

"I know what you're going to say," Dani said without turning around.

"Do you? That's something since *I* don't even know what I'm going to say yet." Claire joined Dani and sat on the edge of the bed. "Tell me what's keeping you from running straight over to Ellie's right now."

"I can't run in these things," Dani joked lamely. "Sorry. What if I make things worse, Claire?"

"How could you possibly do that?"

"By saying the wrong thing! And don't pretend I'm not, like, the queen of saying the wrong thing. I certainly can't bake a damn pie to make it all better. What am I supposed to do?"

"Dani, look at me. Maybe what you need to do for Ellie is exactly what Ellie did for you."

Dani frowned in confusion. "That's exactly what I just told you I *couldn't* do! I can't be Ellie!"

"No, but you can be yourself. That's who Ellie was with you. You don't need to be anyone but yourself with her. Be the Dani she knows. Surly, pig-headed, blunt Dani."

"Uh . . . thanks?"

Claire smiled. "You're welcome. Can't deny it, can you?"

Dani sighed. "No. Do you think that will work?"

"I don't know. I mean, it sounds like she's pretty surly herself." Claire shrugged. "Maybe that's what Ellie will understand. Especially coming from someone who knows firsthand what life is like without legs."

"Jessie!" Dani called out.

"Yeah!" After a brief knock, Jessie poked her head around the door. "Will you go?"

"I want to know everything that her doctor said about her paralysis. Is that okay?"

"Yeah, of course. I'll tell you on the way."

"Claire has to drive me." Dani climbed up on the bed and began taking her shorties off. "I'm using the wheelchair."

"Why?" Claire and Jessie asked at the same time.

"Because Ellie needs to be reminded that she still has hers. Plus, she's in a wheelchair. We'll be, like, wheel buddies."

Jessie snickered. "Look, if it works, I'm all for it. Get dressed, and let's go."

"You got your mom's bossiness!" Dani shouted at a retreating Jessie.

"God, I hope I'm doing the right thing." Dani inhaled sharply, holding her breath for a moment, then letting it out slowly. "If this backfires, am I allowed to blame you?"

"Absolutely not," Claire answered haughtily. "I merely gave advice. *You* chose to take it."

"Typical," Dani muttered.

"Keep it up, *babe,* and I'll make you get the wheelchair out of the back."

Dani laughed. "Thanks a lot! So, I'm, uh, going to tell Ellie that the prosthetics are being adjusted." She had been agonizing about her decision *not* to wear her prosthetics the entire drive over to Ellie's. This whole "making adult decisions" was hard, and Dani didn't want to do it anymore. But she had to for Ellie.

"Okay, but why not tell her the truth?"

"I dunno. I want Ellie to, like, open up to me. Ya know? There's tough love, and then there's being mean. I don't wanna just pop in there and say, 'at least you're not missing yours,' right?"

Claire nodded. "Right. That would probably have a negative outcome. Have you been going over what you're going to say this whole time?"

"Yep."

"Are you driving yourself crazy?"

"Yep." Dani scrubbed her face with her hands. "Damn it. I wish I could bake!"

Claire laughed. "I wish you could, too. But Ellie doesn't need pie from you, babe. She just needs you to tell her it will all be okay."

"What if it's not? What if she can't walk ever again?"

Claire glanced over at Dani. "Then you tell her it will all be okay. You tell her that it will be hard and painful, but she can live a full, wonderful life without her legs. Unless you don't believe that yourself?"

Dani thought about what it was like waking up without legs. How she had wished she had died instead. Then Dani thought about the last couple of weeks. If she had died, *if* she had given up, she would never have known what it was like to be with Claire again. In every way. Dani was still learning how to cope — how to live fully — without legs. But she was learning with the person she loved most in the world. Ellie needed to be reminded that she had so many people in her life that loved her. If Ellie opened herself back up to them, everything *would* be okay.

Dani reached over and took Claire's free hand. "I believe it."

Blaise knocked on Claire's window and waved. "Why didn't you come inside?" she asked once the window was down.

"Oh, I didn't want to intrude."

"That's silly. You're family. Come on. It's not my house, but I'm inviting you in because I'm sure Hunter would love to see you."

Claire smiled. "Thank you. But since you brought up family, could I ask you a favor?"

"Of course." Blaise leaned her elbows on the door. "What's up?"

Claire took a breath. "Okay, by intruding, I mean on Dani's time with Ellie. I didn't come in with her because I didn't want Dani to use me as a crutch. She's been making some tough decisions lately, but sometimes she doubts herself when I'm around."

"So, you want me to knock some sense into her?" Blaise teased since Claire had yet to ask her favor.

"No!" Claire laughed. "Well, maybe. Anyway, I was hoping you could give Dani a ride home once she's finished talking with Ellie."

"Sure, I could. Does that mean you're leaving and not accepting my invitation into a house that isn't mine?"

Claire snorted with laughter. Man, she loved Blaise and her wit! "Yeah, but only because I want Dani to spend time with you all. She needs to know that I'm not her only family. When she found out that Rita — her incubator — moved away, she felt lost and alone. Like she wasn't a part of anything anymore. She *knows* I'm there, but I think she needs more."

"Claire, I'm sure Dani appreciates everything you're doing

for her," Blaise soothed, thinking Claire felt sad about Dani maybe needing more.

"Oh, I know she does. No, no, you're misunderstanding." Claire cleared her throat and tried again. "She didn't tell me she needed more. *I* think that. She needs a mother figure. She has that with Ellie. She needs a cool aunt." Claire smiled at Blaise. "That's where you come in. She needs sisters."

"Jessie and Piper," Blaise guessed, proud of her "cool aunt" status.

Claire nodded. "I want her to know she's not alone anymore. And losing Rita doesn't mean *she's* lost. I want her to know that family goes further than the one you were born into."

Blaise patted Claire on the shoulder amicably. "You're pretty damn smart, kiddo. So, yeah, I'd be happy to take Dani home. What do you want me to tell her when she asks where you went?"

"The truth. I have some work to finish. And now that the apartment it quiet, it's a perfect time."

"And Dani needs quality time with her cool aunt," Blaise grinned. "Go on, sweets. I got you covered. We'll make sure Dani knows she is right where she belongs."

Later that night, Dani lay in bed, staring up at the ceiling. Claire was naked, snuggled up beside her, and Dani felt better than she had in years. After the visit Dani had with Ellie, Hunter, Jessie, and Blaise, she was flying high. It almost seemed crazy now that she had had such anxiety before the drive across town. That anxiety turned to happiness on the way back home. Dani felt like she was a part of a family again. Or perhaps for the first time since her dad died. Right now, Dani was at a point where she could believe she was getting stronger — mentally and physically. Of course, she knew she had a long way to go still, but this was a great start.

The best part of this day, however, was when she got home. She excitedly told Claire everything that went on over at Hunter's — leaving nothing out. Dani had been proud of herself and the way she handled things with Ellie. When Claire echoed that sentiment and rewarded Dani with finishing what they had started in the shower, Dani's heart soared.

Claire moved slightly, letting out a little snore as she did. Dani smiled. She had been listening to the small noises Claire made for months. Having them right in her ear now made them even more endearing. Dani was listening carefully for more when the ding of Claire's phone startled her.

"Who the hell is texting at this hour?" Dani grumbled.

Claire stirred. "Huh?"

"Shit, sorry." Dani hadn't realized she asked her question out loud. "Didn't mean to wake you."

"S'okay. What's . . ." Claire's phone dinged again. "Who the heck?" Claire rolled over to check her messages, smiling at Dani's continued grumbling. Her smile widened when she saw the news. "It's Jessie. Ellie and Hunter got engaged."

"Whoa! What?!"

Claire rolled back over to an excited Dani. "Jessie wants me to thank you for whatever you said to her mom. It helped Ellie a lot."

Dani thrust her arms in the air, her stumps bouncing jubilantly on the bed as she did a little happy dance. After a minute, she calmed down and glanced over at Claire. "I did good."

It wasn't a question, but Claire felt the need to answer Dani's happy declaration. "You did good, baby."

EPILOGUE

"Ready?" Claire stuffed a manuscript in her bag. Today was the day! The day that Dani will finally meet — and talk — with Jos. Dani had gone back and forth on whether she really wanted to do this. But after a bit of coaxing from Claire, Dani stopped resisting.

"Yep. Let's do this!" Dani grabbed the top of the small kitchen island and pulled herself up. She rested on one elbow as she swiped Claire's keys off the counter and tossed them to her girlfriend.

Claire raised a brow. "You just wanted to show off your new muscles by doing that."

Dani hopped down, landing on her newly heightened shorties. Another inch closer to getting her permanent prosthetics.

"Don't pretend you don't think they're sexy." She flexed her biceps. "Especially in bed while I'm . . ."

"Xena Warrior Princess!" Claire shouted in surprise. She had been laughing as she was opening the front door. That laughter abruptly stopped when she saw her father's face.

"Excuse me?" Jose said in confusion.

"Uh, Xena marathon has been playing on SYFY," Dani said as if that explained everything. Meanwhile, her cheeks were on fire from the blush that most likely spanned her entire body. Not that there was much of it. *Jesus.* How much did he hear?

"Yeah, that didn't clear anything up." Jose looked from his

daughter to Dani and back again. They were both beet red as though he had walked in on . . . and since he *never* wanted to think about his little girl in any kind of "situation," he quickly changed the subject. "I, uh, need to talk to Dani."

That sounded serious. Whatever it was, Dani didn't think she wanted to hear it. "I, like, have an appointment we're trying to get to."

"It's important, Dani," Jose insisted.

"So is this, um, meeting. It's with Claire's boss. Can't be late for that, ya know."

Claire studied her father's expression. He only looked that somber when he was in lawyer mode. What if this had something to do with what happened to Dani? "I can text Jos and tell her we're going to be a little delayed," Claire suggested.

Dani gave Claire the side-eye, then sighed when Claire gave her a look. "Yeah, okay." She walked back into the living room and plopped herself on the couch moodily.

Claire rolled her eyes for her dad's sake. "Come in and ignore Dani's rudeness."

Jose chuckled. "You make it out to be like I haven't known this kid for more than half her life. I'm more used to that attitude than anything else."

"I ain't got an attitude," Dani groused. Of course, Claire gave her another look for saying "ain't" and Dani apologized. "What's this about?" she asked Jose, hoping he hadn't heard what they were talking about at the front door. How freakin' embarrassing.

Jose settled himself onto the chair and placed a manila folder on the coffee table. "Claire, maybe you could give us a few minutes alone."

"There ain't, ahem, isn't anything you can say that Claire can't hear, Pops."

Jose glanced at his daughter, then back at Dani. "This has to do with your time out on Skid Row, Dani."

Dani shrugged. "She knows all about it."

Jose nodded once. He wasn't too keen on his daughter hearing all he has to say, but ultimately, it was Dani's decision. And Claire's, of course. "Alright. Dani, do you know a young lady by the name of," Jose checked the file he brought with him. "Alba Murataj?"

Dani frowned. "Uh, no."

"Are you sure? She was with a gang that was called The Pharmacy around Skid Row."

"I'm sorry, Pops, but I don't know anyone by that name." Thank goodness. She knew of The Pharmacy, of course. However, confessing to that meant admitting to what she did out there.

"Dad, they wouldn't know names out there," Claire explained.

Stop helping, Claire! Dani thought with a healthy bit of fear.

"What do you mean?"

"Well, names weren't used. Something about it being too personal."

"Claire!" Dani couldn't believe Claire was ratting her out!

"What? Dani, if this has to do with what happened to you, Dad needs to know! Maybe you *do* know this person, but the name doesn't sound familiar to you because . . ."

"I got it, no names," Jose cut in. He was determined now to find out what Dani was so afraid of. He flipped the file to a photo and showed it to Dani. "Do you know her?"

Dani flinched violently. "That's no freakin' lady," she spat. "That's Viper."

Claire snatched the file out of her father's hand. *So this is the bitch?*

"Viper," Jose repeated. "How well do you know her?"

Dani's eyes darted to Claire. Well, hell. She didn't want Claire to know *that!*

"Hang on," Claire exclaimed before Dani could answer. She had figured out that Viper had sunk her fangs into Dani when she read Dani's letters. Though it made her sick, she couldn't get mad at Dani. Hadn't Claire spent months with Cris? But there were more important things to worry about. "Dani wants immunity."

Claire dug something out of her pocket and handed it to a very confused Dani.

"Wha . . .?"

"Give it to Dad." Claire took Dani's hand and held it out to her dad. "Dani would like to hire you."

"I would?"

"Claire, what's going on?"

"Dani wants to hire you." Claire widened her eyes at Dani, willing her to catch onto her plan. "That means whatever she says to you is protected by the attorney-client privilege."

Like a wallop to the head, Dani finally caught on. "Right." She thrust whatever Claire had put in her hand at Jose.

Jose took the bill and looked at it. "You think you can hire me for five dollars?"

"Yes," Claire answered with authority.

"Dani? Is this what you want?" Dani nodded. Jose sighed

and stuffed the bill in his pocket. "Will you answer my question now?"

"Will she get immunity?"

Jose sighed again. "Claire Bear, no one is trying to punish Dani for anything. What I'm here for has nothing to do with whatever she did out there." He turned his attention back on Dani. "We received an anonymous tip about the night you were hit. My contact at the LAPD told me about it thinking you would be more comfortable talking to me. If you could corroborate some things, it would be helpful."

"I — I don't remember anything about that."

"Dani," Claire said softly.

Dammit. "What do you want to know?" Dani asked carefully.

"You knew this Viper person?"

"Yes."

"Were you close?"

Dani's eyes flickered to Claire's again. "Not really."

"Dani, it's okay," Claire said, taking her hand. "Tell Dad the truth. About everything."

God, Dani hoped Claire was right about it being okay. "I'm sorry," she said to Jose.

"For what?"

"What I'm going to tell you. You're going to hate me."

Jose leaned over and took Dani's hand. "Dani, I may not like what I hear about your time out there. But I could never fault you for whatever you did to survive."

Dani wanted to believe that was true. Whether it was or wasn't, she knew she had to do this. For Claire. For herself.

"Viper made big promises to me. Promises that made me betray who I am and the people who took care of me out there. I was desperate enough and tired enough to believe her. I became her pack mule. She'd give me an address, and I'd pick up a package and bring it back to her."

"Did you know what was in the packages?" Jose asked cautiously.

"I pretended I didn't," Dani answered truthfully. "Not to fool her, but to try and fool myself. But I knew."

Jose nodded. "Where did you take them? Could you point it out on a map?"

Dani shook her head. "I could give you an address, but who knows if they're still there."

"Okay." Jose flipped to a page that was a typed transcript. "The anonymous caller said Viper," he used the street name to keep Dani's focus, "is the person who ran over you." He looked up at Dani. "The police need more evidence than an anonymous tip to check that out. Can you tell me anything about that night? Or if Viper had reason to try to kill you?"

Though Jose was trying hard to sound professional, Dani heard the small crack in his voice. Somehow that made her feel better. He still cared if he got emotional.

"After a friend of mine OD'ed, I told Viper I was done. That I wasn't running any packages for her or the Pharmacy anymore. And that I didn't want to be with her anymore. She said it wasn't as easy as that. People don't just leave when they want to. That it's *her* decision." Dani fidgeted. "I didn't care. I wanted out, so I stopped. That night, I went looking for Angel, hoping she'd forgive me and put me back under her protection."

"Who's Angel?"

Dani shook her head. "It doesn't matter. I don't know her real name, and she's not a part of this. I shouldn't have said that name, so please, leave her out of it."

Jose agreed reluctantly. "What can you tell me about the accident."

"It wasn't an accident, Daddy! And I swear, this Viper chick better not get a deal! She needs to be punished for what she did to Dani!"

Jose's eyebrows rose. "So you *do* remember? And you know for certain it was this Viper person?"

"Yes," Dani answered slowly. "I saw her behind the wheel."

Jose's nostrils flared with hatred for some young person he didn't know. "What about the car? Can you remember anything about it?" He took out a pen, ready to write.

"It was black, but not shiny. A muscle car of some sort. Older. Like, um, a Charger, or something." Dani closed her eyes and concentrated. "One of the headlights was out. I remember because I thought it was a motorcycle at first. The grill had a hole in it. I don't remember the license plate, but I know it had, like, a Z. Maybe a 0, I don't know."

"That's okay. That's real good, Dani." Jose flipped to another photo. "There's a car registered in this Viper person's name. But it's not a Charger." He handed it to Dani, and she dropped it like it was a hot piece of coal."

"*That's the car,*" Dani barely whispered.

Jose took note that the Challenger in the photo was indeed the one that hit Dani that night. He nodded to Claire, who immediately enveloped Dani in a hug. She poured every bit of her compassion into that hug.

"Do you have everything you need?" Claire asked.

"I think so. At least enough to start an investigation. Dani? Will you be willing to testify if it comes to that, Dani?"

Dani felt Claire squeeze her hand. The hand that not long ago was wrapped in a cast. The hand that took pins and screws just to put it back together.

"Yeah. I'll testify."

Jos sat back in the booth and blew out a breath. The girl in front of her wasn't even twenty years old and yet, she's lived a lifetime of heartache. The miracle was how sweet Dani was. Awkward at times, but Jos was used to that. Hell, she was awkward herself.

"I appreciate you talking to me, Dani." Initially, Jos had been irritated with being put on hold yet again. But the story Dani just told Joselyn Cohan — the writer — was well worth the wait.

Dani shrugged shyly. "I'm just sorry it took so long for us to get together. Life took another unexpected turn. Anyway, I don't know how much good it did, me talking to you about my time on the streets. I'm not a very good storyteller."

Jos smiled genuinely. "Good thing I am, then, eh?" She began packing her stuff up. They had been at the diner now for close to five hours, and she was sure Dani was getting tired of her. Even so, Dani had given her quite a bit to sort through. Fortunately, it had all the ingredients for a great book. What was unfortunate was the fact that Dani had to live it.

"Did I give you enough stuff to work with?" Dani asked, obviously unaware of Jos's thoughts.

"You sure did. I do, however, hope it'd be okay if I contacted you now and then while writing the book. Sometimes I like to know what a real emotion would be in certain situations."

"Yeah, sure. No problem. So, like, will the book be about homelessness or something?"

Jos smiled. "The book will be about a teenaged girl who was forced to live an incredibly difficult life. A young woman who, despite being homeless and losing her legs, learns how to love, live, and trust again. Who, in the end, comes out on top."

Dani stared at Jos unblinkingly. "You're writing a book about *me?* Like, for real me?"

"I am." Jos hesitated. "Unless you don't want me to?" Jos didn't stop to think about how this news would affect Dani. It was one of the downfalls of being a writer. Sometimes you saw the story before anything else. "I apologize. I get a little zealous when I get an idea in my head. The words scream to get out, which means they sometimes drown out the feelings of those around me."

"Well, I don't know what zealous means, but I think it's freakin' cool that you're writing a book about me!" Dani leaned into the table, nearly knocking over the glass of milk she needed to finish. "Can I choose the names of mine and Claire's characters?"

Jos laughed. "How about this. You give me suggestions, and I'll see if they work."

Dani grinned. "Deal! Do you want to know how the story ends?"

Jos looked around them, wondering if there was something she had missed during their candid conversation. "I thought this was a good ending. You, sitting here, happy."

"Well, sure. But you gotta wrap things up, right? Like what happened to Viper? Or did I ever find my mother?"

This time Jos leaned in. "I was so engrossed in everything else, I forgot about those things! So? What happened?" Jos, an avid reader, as well as a writer, could hardly contain her excitement. She felt as though she were on the last page of a novel, reading with bated breath to learn the fate of those who had wronged the protagonist.

Dani pulled out her phone. She navigated to a news site, then flipped it around to show the writer. "Remember when I said life took another unexpected turn? Viper was arrested for attempted murder and drug charges. I think they just tacked on the drug charges for fun. Anyway, I guess she made some enemies. Or maybe someone was afraid she'd talk. She was shanked while waiting for her trial to begin." Dani stared at the picture of the girl she knew only as Viper. The girl who antagonized her, bullied her, slept with her, and nearly killed her. "I should feel something now that she's gone, but I don't. I mean, I'm kinda sorry she doesn't have to sit in jail for a long time. But she took my legs from me. She ran me over intending to kill me. Why should I care she's dead? Does that make me a bad person?"

Jos took Dani's phone and laid it on the table facing down. "I think it makes you human. Your feelings are just that, Dani. Yours. No one can dictate what they should be."

Dani mulled that over for a bit before nodding. "Will you kill the villain in your book?"

Jos tilted her head and thought about that. "I don't know. It's something I'll have to let come naturally once I get to the end. Would you be disappointed if I don't?"

Dani shook her head. "Nah. A harsh sentence would have satisfied me in real life. I think it'd satisfy me in my fictional life, too."

Jos smiled. "We'll just see how it goes then. What about your mother? Did you find her?"

"Mr. Oliver did. She's worse off than she was when I was with her. He called her gaunt. I had to look that up. Part of me hates that she's suffering. But I can remove that as easily as removing my prosthetics. Mr. Oliver got me a few of my dad's things. That's all I really care about. Rita threw away her right to my sympathy when she threw me away." Dani frowned. "Maybe you shouldn't write that. People may think the character is cold-hearted and unwilling to take responsibility for what happened to her."

"I think you underestimate the passion of readers. I've gotten messages about books I've written telling me that I went too easy on the antagonist. You've suffered quite a bit, Dani. I think the readers would want to know that the people who put you in that situation are paying a price for that. As far as your 'responsibility' goes, I think you've paid enough of a price of your own."

"I get why Claire likes you." Dani blushed when Jos smiled sweetly at her. "I, um, I liked talking to you. I kinda feel like a weight has been lifted off my chest a little. If that makes sense."

"It does. Holding things in can allow anger and confusion to build up. It's good to talk, Dani. Be sure both you and Claire remember that. I'm here for you and Claire. It doesn't even have to be book related," Jos winked.

Dani grinned broadly. "Could you do me, like, a huge favor? When you're done, like, writing the book. Could you not put *The End* like they do in other books? That sounds so final to me. I'd like to think Claire and I are starting over."

Starting Over...

ACKNOWLEDGMENTS

This was one of the hardest books I've written during the most difficult time in my life. I'm not used to writing young/new adult! I wrote the Destined vampire trilogy a lifetime ago (it seems). I'm no spring chicken anymore! So, trying to get into the minds of teenagers or new adults isn't that easy. Plus, I was dealing with a subject that I had absolutely no experience with. I did a *ton* of research on this book. Since I'm not a medical doctor or an amputee — or young anymore — I hope I did it justice.

While writing this book, I lost my beloved momma. In losing her, I lost myself. I'm still trying to find who I was before she passed away. Maybe I'll never find that person again or grow into someone new. But one thing I do know is that I'm my momma's daughter. Whomever I become; I will be better simply because of her. She was the strongest woman I've ever known. She loved me unconditionally. She sacrificed for me. She taught me. She made me the woman I became. Everything I do in life that means anything is a tribute to her. I wrote this to my momma in 2018, not long before we had to place her in a nursing home:

Momma,

When I was a little girl, you called me your little frog and loved me unconditionally, teaching me that love is not only skin deep.

When I was a little girl, you said "you can do it" every time I told you what I wanted to be when I grew up, teaching me that dreams were never out of reach.

When I was a little girl, you didn't eat so that I could, teaching me the importance of sacrificing for the ones you love.

When I was a little girl, you worked multiple jobs in order to keep a roof over my head, teaching me not to be afraid of hard work.

When I was a little girl, you said nothing when dirt was thrown on you and you were called names, teaching me that sometimes being strong means standing tall instead of fighting back.

When I was a little girl, you laughed and played when we pushed you in the pool wearing the only clothes you had, teaching me to embrace the spontaneity in life.

When I was a little girl, you'd pile us in the car on a whim, teaching me that adventure was never more than a car ride away.

When I was a little girl, we had our problems, but you were always ready with a hug and an "I love you," teaching me that arguments didn't mean I lost your love.

Now that I'm a woman, I still learn from you every day. I still need my mommy. But I am able to love, follow my dreams, compromise and sacrifice, work for what I want in life, stand tall, be spontaneous, and have adventures. It is my turn now to hold you, teach you, love you, be strong for you. You may not always remember who I am to you, but to me you are Wonder Woman, and the greatest love. You are my mom. No matter how much you forget, I will always remember for you.

Love,
Your daughter

Diane Lynnette Payton
October 17, 1949 – March 28, 2020

Daisy — I don't think I could have survived these past couple of months without you. It's impossible to describe how lucky I am to have you in my life.

Wanda — You were there when I needed you the most. Thank you, beastie. I live you do.

Karen — Beastie II. Your continued support means the world to me. Tell Kevin I said "haayy."

Janice — You're always spot on when I need someone to tell me if where I'm going with a book is any good. Thank you for being there.

Lisa — I know that if I make you feel the feelings, I'm doing something right. Thank you for taking the time to read!

Jim — As always, you teach me so much. I'll keep implementing those teachings into my writing.

Shout out to: Aleana, Kim, Earnilia, Nellie, Leo, Florinda, and my "villain" Alba!

My message to my readers — Oh, boy. Where to even begin. You all have been so incredibly supportive, caring, and patient with me. A writer's bread and butter is to punch out those books like they're on Lucille Ball's assembly line. But you all stood by me — understanding — while I navigated through this difficult journey called life and put the writing on hold for a bit. When I wasn't around much online, you all took it upon yourselves to keep our group entertaining. And when I lost my momma, the outpouring of love helped me make it through another day. You inspire me to keep writing. Your compassion shows me — even in the worst of times — that there is good in the world. Thank you. I don't know if that is enough but thank you.

ABOUT THE AUTHOR

I've been in Houston, Texas since 2009 and moving here was one of the best decisions I've ever made. I've been able to live wonderfully and write to my heart's content. Writing novels has always helped me release the voices in my head. Something I truly need. It can get loud in there. :)

I've always enjoyed the arts in one form or another. Music sets the mood, reading stimulates my brain, and writing allows me to utilize my imagination in any way I want. I've been writing stories since I was a teen and figured out writing was my passion when I finished my first novel, Something About Eve.

As a merchandiser for singer/actress Deborah Gibson, I've had the opportunity to be involved in wonderful experiences, travel around the country and meet exciting people. It's experiences like this, I believe, that help me create unique, and (hopefully) lovable characters. I'm also fortunate enough to have recently started a business called Jaded Angels LLC. The company — specializing in custom t-shirts as well as promotional items — was inspired by my mother with a portion of proceeds going to help those living with Alzheimer's.

What's coming next? I have a few stories in my head. We'll see which one speaks the loudest. Until next time, thank you for reading!

WHERE YOU CAN FIND CAMEO CHARACTERS

ELLIE AND HUNTER

Coming Home (Ellie only)
Coming Out (Their story)

PATTY AND MO

Coming Out
Becoming

BLAISE STEELE

Coming Home
Coming Out

PIPER KNIGHT

Coming Home
Coming Out

JESSIE MONTGOMERY

Coming Home
Coming Out

Connect with Jourdyn Kelly online

My Website
(http://www.jourdynkelly.com/)

Twitter
(https://twitter.com/JourdynK)

Goodreads
(http://www.goodreads.com/author/show/
2980644.Jourdyn_Kelly)

Facebook
(https://www.facebook.com/AuthorJourdynKelly)

Secret Society on Facebook
(https://www.facebook.com/groups/JoKels/)

Instagram
(https://www.instagram.com/jourdynk/)

Amazon Author's Page
(http://www.amazon.com/-/e/B005O24HK8)

Printed in Great Britain
by Amazon